# sex
# 365

*Dare you to...*

# sex

## 365

*Dare you to...*

# LONDON • NEW YORK • MUNICH • MELBOURNE • DELHI

**Project editor** Angela Baynham
**Designer** Nigel Wright
**Senior editor** Helen Murray
**Senior art editor** Wendy Bartlet
**Managing editor** Penny Warren
**Managing art editor** Glenda Fisher
**Production editor** Ben Marcus
**Production controller** Man Fai Lau
**Creative technical support** Sonia Charbonnier
**Category publisher** Peggy Vance

First published in Great Britain in 2011 by Dorling Kindersley
Limited, 80 Strand, London, WC2R 0RL Penguin Group (UK)

2 4 6 8 10 9 7 5 3
002-178971-Jan/11

A CIP catalogue of this book is available from
the British Library

ISBN 978-1-4053-6201-6

Colour reproduction by Colourscan, Singapore
Printed and bound by Star Standard, Singapore

Discover more at **www.dk.com**

# contents

# *introduction*

**SEX 365 DARE YOU TO...** is the perfect bed companion for lovers who want to make their sex life more thrilling, naughty, and erotic. Sex dares add a new dimension to sex – they push back your boundaries and force you to be more adventurous and experimental. Plus, if you've got a secret fetish or fantasy you've always been too shy to broach, a dare is a great way to sneak it into your sex life.

Over the next 365 pages you'll discover games, roleplays, techniques, costumes, toys, and positions to shake up your sex life. You'll go on a rude picnic, have sex swinging from the ceiling, attempt unique oral sex positions, tie each other up, perform for each other, and discover erogenous zones you didn't know you had... by the end no sexual challenge will make you blush.

For a whole year of naughtiness, try working your way through the sex dares from number one to 365. The dares get saucier as the book goes on, starting with sweet, sensual, and romantic dares in chapter 1 and finishing with pure kinkiness in chapter 4. Alternatively, if you want to make sex excitingly unpredictable, just turn to pages 382–383, blindfold your lover, and tell him or her to point to a square on the Dare Selector.

Refer to page 381 for everything you'll need to prepare for your 365 nights of pleasure.

You'll quickly find that the nights you have "Dare Sex" are the ones that make you buzz with a thrilling sense of naughtiness. So throw away your inhibitions and dare your lover to do something wicked tonight.

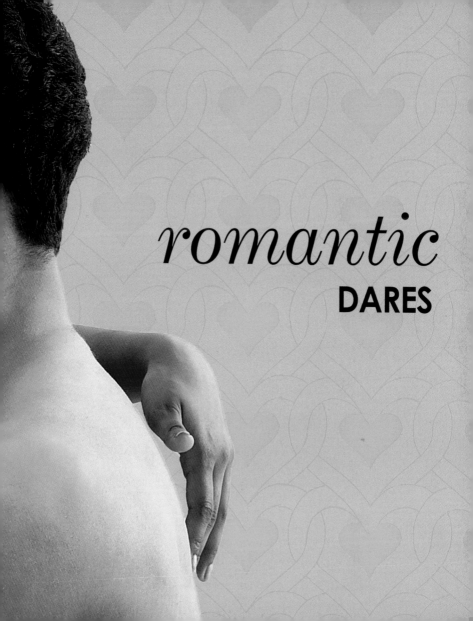

# *romantic*
## DARES

## ...kiss like the first time

# 1

**HER** Pretend we've just met for the first time and pounce on me. Pin me to the wall and kiss me passionately.

**HIM** Abandon yourself to the kiss. Push your body against mine. Leave me breathless.

# ...blow each other's minds

**2**

**HER** Do something to make me really hot, then cool me down by blowing your breath against my skin.

**HIM** Lay me on my back, lick my hotspots, then tease me by blowing them dry.

# ...be a naked servant

**3**

**HER** Dress up as my half-naked butler. Bring me my favourite drink in bed and then lavish me with sexual favours.

**HIM** Ask me to do anything you want... even if it's something kinky.

# ...drive me crazy with your tongue

**4**

**HER** Lie me down on the bed, slide cushions underneath me, then make me delirious with your tongue.

**HIM** Tug my hair and writhe as you get more and more excited.

# ...play artist and model

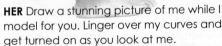

## 5

**HER** Draw a stunning picture of me while I model for you. Linger over my curves and get turned on as you look at me.

**HIM** Let me sketch you from lots of gorgeous angles. Make your poses naughty.

## ...take each other by surprise

**6**

**HER** Slink up behind me, slide your hand over my eyes and whisper "guess who?" in your sexiest voice.

**HIM** Interrupt me when I'm in the middle of something. Make me an offer I can't resist.

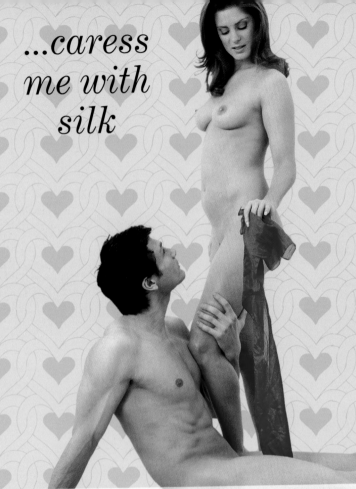

# ...caress me with silk

## 7

**HER** Lie me on my front, caress my bum and back with a silk scarf, then use it to tie my hands behind my back.

**HIM** Make me tingle with silky strokes, then use your scarf to blindfold me.

# ...watch a cheeky movie together

## 8

**HER** Lie down and watch a sexy film with me. Press your bum tight against mine. Caress my cheeks.

**HIM** Caress my back. Let me slip my hand through your thighs so I can stroke you.

# ...lie back and relax

**9**

**HER** Let me take a sex break where I lie back on your thighs, rest my feet on your chest, and savour the sensations.

**HIM** Talk to me. Turn me on by describing your next move in intimate detail.

# ...take a fingertip tour

**10**

**HER** Lie behind me and give me goosebumps by trailing your fingertips seductively over my whole body.

**HIM** Start on my back, then roll me over and explore my front with your fingers.

# ...*make it smooth, sweet, and creamy*

## 11

**HER** Come to bed for dessert. Let me feed you silky smooth ice cream just as it's about to melt.

**HIM** Make sure you drop some ice-cream on me. Use the tip of your tongue to lick it off.

...be a
*foot servant*

# 12

**HER** Give me a long and lingering foot massage, then take my toes softly between your lips and caress them with your tongue.

**HIM** Hold my foot in your hands. Nibble and suck my toes gently at first, then harder.

# ...let your eyes wander

**13**

**HER** Look at me as I lie naked in bed. Gaze longingly at every part of me from my lips to my legs. Tell me your favourite bits.

**HIM** Admire me, too. Pay me the sexiest compliment you can think of.

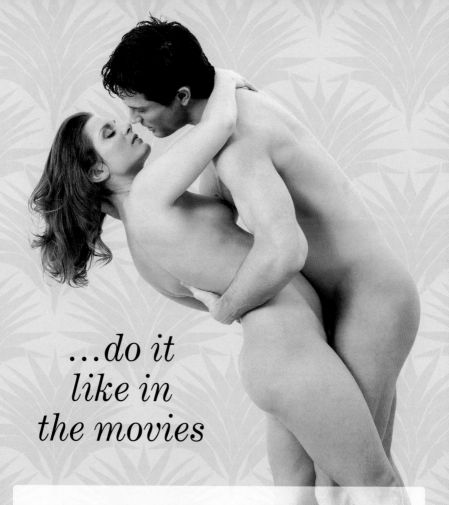

# ...do it like in the movies

## 14

**HER** Take me in your arms and sweep me off my feet. Hold me tight as you kiss me passionately.

**HIM** Give me a long smouldering look before you surrender to my kiss.

*...stay
seductively
still*

## 15

**HER** Let me sit on your lap with you deep inside me. Let's enjoy being joined without any movement.

**HIM** Make all the moves internal. Squeeze me hard with your muscles.

*...have a TLC night*

**16**

**HER** Come to bed early for an evening of strokes, cuddles, and caresses.

**HIM** Hold my head against your gorgeous breasts. Kiss my head while you gently massage my shoulders.

# ...try some amorous target practice

**17**

**HER** Kneel on the floor and stretch me so my body is taut against yours, then fire your arrow into me.

**HIM** Lean forward and straighten your leg so I can target you with precise accuracy.

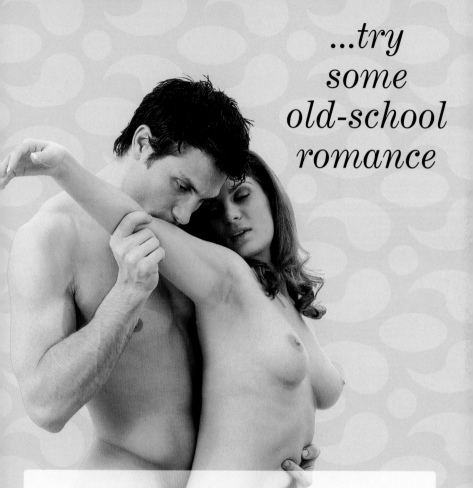

*...try some old-school romance*

**18**

**HER** Stand behind me and tenderly take my arm. Kiss it softly from wrist to shoulder.

**HIM** Play the part of being coy and innocent, but allow yourself to be overwhelmed, too.

# ...have a cocktail party for two

## 19

**HER** Help me to invent a sexy new cocktail. Get messy with me as we squeeze, crush, and shake the ingredients.

**HIM** Pour the cocktail into a single glass, bring it to bed, and drink it naked with me.

# ...try some summer lovin'

## 20

**HER** Lie down in the grass on a balmy summer night so I can slide my body on top of yours.

**HIM** Move slinkily on top of me as the sun goes down.

# ...go on a rude picnic

**21**

**HER** Let's go somewhere secluded and then feed each other fresh strawberries and passion fruit.

**HIM** Bring a rug so we can lie down and lick the juice off each other after we've eaten.

# ...bare your soles

## 22

**HER** Give me a foot rub with a difference – slide your foot between my legs at the same time.

**HIM** Rub my feet with your warm, oiled hands then kiss your way up my legs.

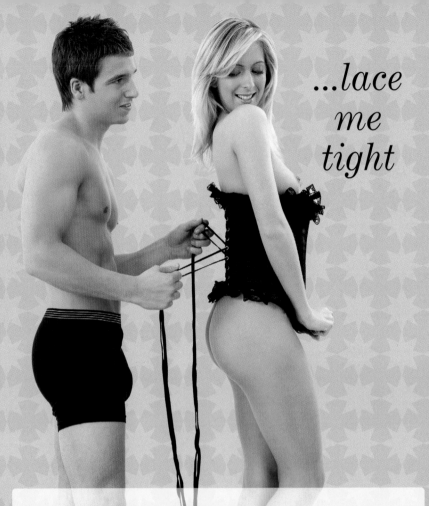

...lace
me
tight

# 23

**HER** Make it your job to lace me into a sexy black corset, but make sure your hands wander along the way.

**HIM** Let me untie you at the end of the evening and have my way with you.

# ...sprinkle the sheets with petals

## 24

**HER** Bring out the red satin sheets and sprinkle them with red rose petals. Make sweet love to me all night.

**HIM** Let's roll around in abandon and crush the petals with our bodies.

*...stage a romantic rescue*

## 25

**HER** Surprise me: be my sexy fireman. Pick me up, throw me over your shoulder, and carry me to the bedroom.

**HIM** When we get to the bedroom, roll around in bed with me. Set me on fire.

# ...try a twist on rear entry

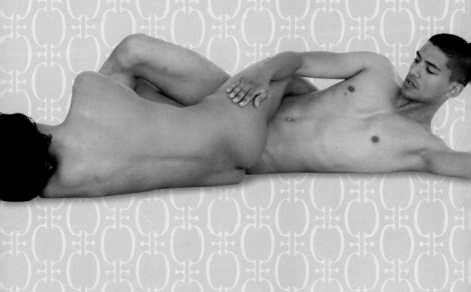

## 26

**HER** Let's head in different directions: I hook my leg over your waist and face your toes while you enter me deeply.

**HIM** Lift your leg a little so I can thrill you with my moves.

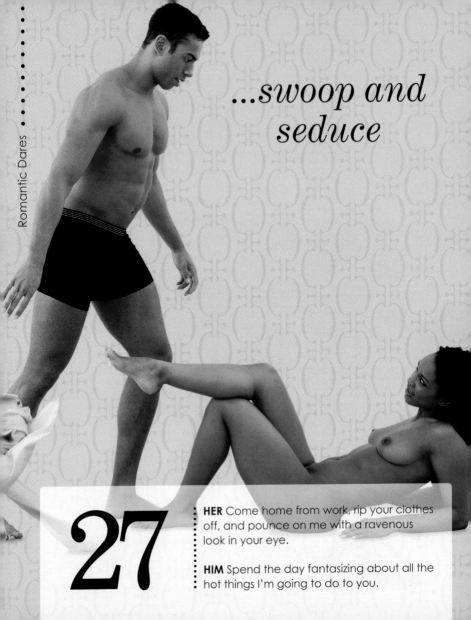

# ...*swoop and seduce*

## 27

**HER** Come home from work, rip your clothes off, and pounce on me with a ravenous look in your eye.

**HIM** Spend the day fantasizing about all the hot things I'm going to do to you.

# ...take it lying down

## 28

**HER** Let me straddle you in a sexy sitting position then lower my body so I'm lying down with you still inside me.

**HIM** Ripple your hips slowly up and down so it feels fantastic for both of us.

# ...bend over backward with lust

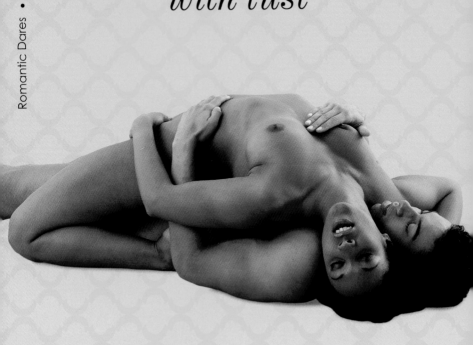

## 29

**HER** Slide your hands in long strokes along my front as I stretch my body over yours. Caress my breasts and nipples.

**HIM** When I'm exploding with desire, let me roll you over so I can take you from behind.

# ...stop at heavy petting

**30**

**HER** Hold me, kiss me, and turn me on with strokes and caresses. Then stop…

**HIM** Tease me and make me sex hungry all week. Then spend the whole weekend in bed with me.

*...teasingly undress me*

# 31

**HER** Undo one button at a time while you kiss my neck and whisper in my ear. Let my dress fall to the floor, then pull me close.

**HIM** Undo my trousers as you kiss me. Kneel as you slide my trousers down my legs.

# ...lick me all over

**32**

**HER** Sprinkle edible body dust all over my naked body. Then find out where I really love being licked.

**HIM** Make a line of dust from my head to my toes. Lick it off slowly.

# ...shower me with flowers

## 33

**HER** Treat me to the ultimate sensual seduction – cover my eyes then sprinkle soft, velvety petals on my skin.

**HIM** Crush your body against mine to release the gorgeous scent from the petals.

*...do the one-hand manoeuvre*

## 34

**HER** Kiss me so hard I don't notice you undoing my bra with one hand. Slide the straps off my shoulders...

**HIM** Undo my trousers in the same way. Slip your hand inside.

# ...give a shampoo seduction

**35**

**HER** Let me lie between your legs as you "shampoo" coconut oil into my hair.

**HIM** Swap places, then after you've given me a head massage, let's get wrapped up together in a warm towel.

# ...offer
## sexual healing

**36**

**HER** Let me seduce you when you're bed-bound. Just lie there without moving and I'll slide on top of you.

**HIM** Let me feel your breasts crushed against my chest.

# ...have a Tantric night

## 37

**HER** Hold me close so I can feel your breath mingling with mine. Get high on sexual energy with me.

**HIM** Make me shiver by drawing your fingertips slowly up my spine.

# ...drizzle warm wax

## 38

**HER** Use massage candles to light the room. Then blow them out one by one and pour the warm wax on me.

**HIM** Let me slide up and down your body to rub the wax in.

## ...play on the stairs

**39**

**HER** Have naughty sex on the stairs with me while I hold on tight to the banister.

**HIM** Let's try other positions, too. Stand on the first step and lean forward while I stand behind you.

# ...give feather pleasure

**40**

**HER** Throw a feather boa around my neck, then pull me towards you for a kiss.

**HIM** Stroke and tickle my naked body with the boa then use it to bind my wrists.

# ...give a sexy wake-up call

## 41

**HER** Turn off the alarm clock and wake me up with your hot body on top of mine.

**HIM** When you're ready, turn over for some passion before breakfast.

# ...have yogi sex

## 42

**HER** Let me sit on your lap, then hug me with your legs. Wrap them tight around me.

**HIM** Wiggle your hips for blissful sensations that ripple through both of us.

# ...try sweet temptation

## 43

**HER** Let's get sticky by feeding each other cake in bed. Kiss me between mouthfuls.

**HIM** Gaze into my eyes while you lick the icing with the tip of your tongue.

# ...carry on in the morning

## 44

**HER** Let's make love in spoons position, then fall asleep with our bodies entwined. Stay close to me all night.

**HIM** Let's have gorgeous wake-up sex first thing in the morning.

# ...turn each other to putty

## 45

**HER** Blow my mind with a sensual massage that goes on and on. Cover every bit of my body with your hands.

**HIM** Press down hard with your hands. Brush me with your lips, hair, and breasts, too.

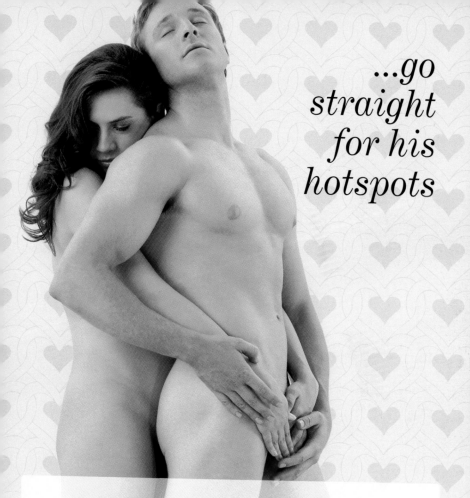

*...go straight for his hotspots*

## 46

**HER** Let me snuggle against your back while I slide one hand around your penis and cup your balls with the other.

**HIM** Press tightly against me so I can feel your hot body. Nibble and bite my neck.

# ...have a sexy heart to heart

**47**

**HER** Come close and wrap your arms around me. Feel our hearts beating faster as the passion mounts.

**HIM** Let's melt into the hug, then sink to the floor and carry on.

# ...pay lip service

# 48

**HER** Lie back and bask in bliss as I trace the outline of your lips with my fingertips.

**HIM** Slip your fingers a little way into my mouth so I can suck and bite them.

## ...make the L-shape

**49**

**HER** Pull me up onto your lap and enter me deeply. Let me stretch my legs up along your body.

**HIM** Open your legs so I can press forward and kiss your body.

## ...do it Hawaiian style

# 50

**HER** Turn up the heat and seduce me with flowers, music, and delicious cocktails.

**HIM** Come close and dance with me. Circle your hips seductively. Let's find a sexy rhythm together.

## ...be a sexy shower attendant

# 51

**HER** Wait for me to come out of the shower and then dry me with a warm towel. Pay special attention to my erogenous bits.

**HIM** Press your body against me so I get hot and wet, too.

# ...be slow and yearning

## 52

**HER** Let's have slow and delicious foreplay. Tease me with lots of lingering kisses and tender strokes.

**HIM** Tell me how much you want me in a whisper. Let me lift you onto my lap.

*...call in late for work*

**53**

**HER** You're fresh out of the shower. I'm in my underwear. We both look irresistible so let's jump on each other.

**HIM** Let's fall into bed and make it fast, wild, and passionate.

# ...spend Sunday in bed

## 54

**HER** Keep the curtains closed and let's have lazy sex all day long.

**HIM** Let's make it a day of sexy treats: erotic movies, massages, cuddles, naughty conversations, then dinner in bed.

## ...share the perfect kiss

# 55

**HER** Caress my face, then slide your fingers up through my hair and pull me gently towards you. Let your lips linger on mine.

**HIM** Tilt your face up to meet mine and gently open your mouth to greet me.

# ...whisper something naughty

## 56

**HER** Lie on top of me and whisper something exciting: a fantasy, a proposition, a dare...

**HIM** Whisper something back, but make it even naughtier. I promise I'll act on it.

# ...give the sexiest welcome home

**57**

**HER** When you get home from work, take all your clothes off and come straight to the bedroom. I'll be waiting for you.

**HIM** Pull back the sheet so I can look at your gorgeous body before I jump in.

*...have a private masked ball*

**58**

**HER** Fill the bedroom with flickering candlelight and dance with me. Wear only your mask.

**HIM** Pretend to be a mysterious stranger. I'll fulfil your fantasies and you fulfil mine.

# ...play Tarzan and Jane

## 59

**HER** Don't give me any choice – just sweep me up in your strong manly arms and take me to bed.

**HIM** Surrender to me. Let me throw you onto the bed and ravish you.

# ...do it xx times in a row

# 60

**HER** Let's have a night of pure lust and keep going until we're spent.

**HIM** Roll onto your side so I can press my body into yours for the final climax.

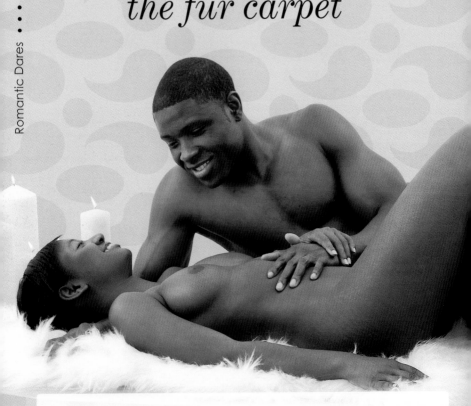

# ...roll out the fur carpet

## 61

**HER** Let's make sweet candlelit love on a fur rug with soft romantic music playing in the background.

**HIM** Let's get intimate – kissing and stroking each other for at least an hour.

*...get wrapped up in each other*

**62**

**HER** Pull me inside your coat on a cold day. Give me your body heat and warm me up with a heartfelt kiss.

**HIM** Let's go home and get even hotter under the covers.

*...say
hello
with
a kiss*

## 63

**HER** Greet me by lifting up my chin with your hand, and giving me an adoring kiss.

**HIM** Respond by snaking your arms around my waist and pulling me towards you. Pretend we're in a world of our own.

*...rise to the occasion*

**64**

**HER** Make your body into a sexy ramp that I can slide and glide on.

**HIM** Use your leg power to push up and down on me until I can't take it any more.

# ...give a mutual massage

## 65

**HER** Give me a glorious, sensual massage. Smooth your oiled palms across my back.

**HIM** Caress my back with your feet as I massage you. Make my body tingle by pressing hard against my buttocks.

# ...deliver a tongue-lashing

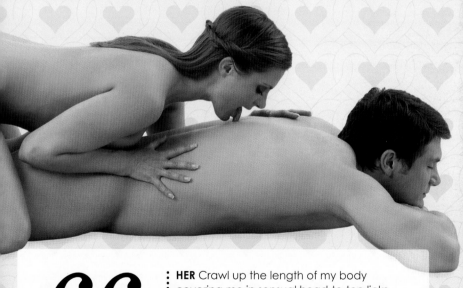

**66**

**HER** Crawl up the length of my body covering me in sensual head-to-toe licks.

**HIM** Return the favour. Flick your tongue all over me until I turn over and grab you.

*...be
music to
her ears*

# 67

**HER** Make me shiver all over. Nibble one ear lobe and caress the other. Whisper seductively to me, too.

**HIM** Bask in the pleasure, then turn to face me for a full-on kiss.

*...try it shaken, not stirred*

**68**

**HER** Be my sexy cocktail-shaking barman. Promise to serve me all evening while I lie back and enjoy myself.

**HIM** Make sure you flirt outrageously with me all the time I'm waiting on you.

# ...make a love knot

## 69

**HER** Let me wrap my body tightly around yours in a romantic clinch. Put your hands under my bum and pull me towards you.

**HIM** When things get intense, push me back and press your body on top of mine.

# ...go to bed at lunch time

**70**

**HER** Let's skip lunch and go to bed for some hot smooching.

**HIM** After some sexy cuddles, let's get entwined for a breathless quickie before we get on with the day.

*...share the look of love*

## 71

**HER** Instead of saying hello when we meet, hold me in your arms so we can share a long, passionate gaze.

**HIM** Don't break the sexy silence. Let's just go straight to bed.

# ...prolong that moment

**72**

**HER** Get really close, as if you're going to kiss me. Then tantalize me by holding your lips just a hair's breadth away from mine.

**HIM** Do nothing. Let the sexual tension stretch to breaking point.

# ...do the breast stroke

**73**

**HER** Let me stroke my body along yours, with my breasts caressing your back and my hands fondling your front.

**HIM** Rub oil into me first so you easily slip and slide all over me.

# ...give a kissing tutorial

## 74

**HER** Let me pull you towards me so I can demonstrate my favourite kissing techniques.

**HIM** Come up for air, then I'll match your techniques with some of my own.

# ...enjoy laid-back love

**75**

**HER** Let me have a sexy chill-out in the middle of sex. Close your eyes and savour the erotic connection.

**HIM** I'll stroke your thighs while you turn your head to kiss my calves.

*... fit together like a jigsaw*

**76**

**HER** Kneel down and let me sit on your lap. I'll mould my body to the shape of yours.

**HIM** Let me slide deep inside you while I stroke your belly with one hand and smooth my other hand up your leg.

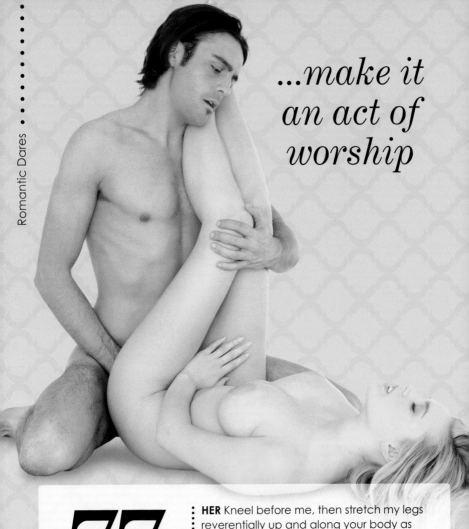

*...make it an act of worship*

## 77

**HER** Kneel before me, then stretch my legs reverentially up and along your body as you deeply enter me.

**HIM** Let me devote myself to your pleasure as I feast my eyes upon your body.

# ...make a pleasure seat

## 78

**HER** Let me lie back in your lap while you lavish sensual treats on the front of my body and nibble my neck.

**HIM** Turn around and kiss your way down my body, starting with my lips.

*...go head to head*

# 79

**HER** Press your forehead to mine as I climb on top and make passionate love to you.

**HIM** Take complete control of me. Make me moan with your rippling moves.

# ...try "the seal"

## 80

**HER** Let me rest on your thighs as I stretch forward. Make me shiver by licking and blowing my back.

**HIM** Squeeze me tight between your thighs. Slowly rock your hips up and down.

# *playful*
## DARES

# ....give the golden touch

## 81

**HER** Let's play with body paint. Leave a naughty trail of handprints all over my breasts, belly, and bum.

**HIM** Make me gold by pressing your body hard against mine.

# ...do the full monty

**82**

**HER** Tease and turn me on by doing a playful strip to some sexy music.

**HIM** Wolf whistle and clap from your front row seat. Give me a standing ovation at the end of my performance.

*...be a swinger for the night*

**83**

**HER** Turn the bedroom into an erotic adventure playground – fix a bar on the ceiling for me to swing from.

**HIM** Let's spend the whole night working on your sexual acrobatic skills.

# ...do it flamenco style

# 84

**HER** Play some hot Spanish guitar music. Let me turn you on with some naked flamenco dancing.

**HIM** Titillate me. Twirl and stamp your feet. Let me peek behind your fans.

*...take the law into your own hands*

**85**

**HER** Tell me how bad I've been. Handcuff me and frisk me from head to toe.

**HIM** Come with me. I'm imprisoning you in the bedroom for some very sexy punishment.

# ...try position impossible

**86**

**HER** Get down on your hands and knees and push your bum hard against mine. Now let's try to have sex.

**HIM** If it doesn't work, let me spin round into doggie position.

*...launch a kiss attack*

**87**

**HER** Stand very still while I work my way down your body with my hot red lips.

**HIM** When your kisses drive me over the edge, let me pounce and smudge your lipstick.

# ...make love gymnastic-style

**88**

**HER** Let me sit on your lap so I can stretch forward with you inside me. Hold me in a firm grip as I shiver with pleasure.

**HIM** Give me glorious sensations as you press your taut body across my thighs.

# ...have a Kama Sutra night

## 89

**HER** Bring the *Kama Sutra* to bed so we can try the hottest positions.

**HIM** Get carried away with passion: do it in bed, on the bedroom floor, on the chest of drawers, and up against the wall.

*...give the ultimate come-on*

# 90

**HER** Come into the bedroom to find me pressed naked against the wall with a wicked expression on my face.

**HIM** Turn me on instantly by beckoning me over and wrapping your leg around me.

*...give a
sneaky peek*

**91**

**HER** Wait for me in bed. I'll join you in a
minute. Get ready for a thrilling glimpse.

**HIM** Even better: ring the doorbell, let me
answer, and give me a gorgeous flash as
you stand on the doorstep.

# ...share a strawberry delight

## 92

**HER** Pour cool cream along the length of my spine, then roll strawberries in it.

**HIM** Let me take the strawberry in my teeth and feed it to you.

*...hitch a ride*

**93**

**HER** Undress me, then offer me a piggy back to the bedroom.

**HIM** Press your body against my back as I carry you. Tell me in a whisper how excited you are.

*...enjoy angel lust*

**94**

**HER** Let me be your fallen angel. I'll descend on the bedroom and treat you to some divine kisses.

**HIM** Take me to heaven with your soft lips and fluttering touch.

# ...try some erotic arm wrestling

# 95

**HER** Grab my hand and try to beat me –
I'll distract you by talking dirty.

**HIM** The winner's privilege is the sexual
favour of his or her choice.

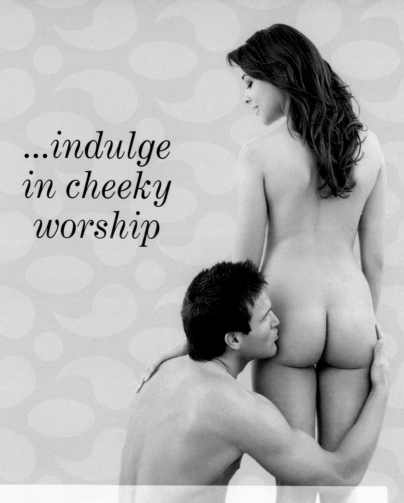

*...indulge in cheeky worship*

# 96

**HER** Kneel at my feet as you playfully nuzzle, nip, and nibble my buttocks.

**HIM** Return the favour as I lie on my front. Caress me with your lips and breasts.

# ...try Ben Wa balls

## 97

**HER** Make love to me after I've spent the day wearing love balls – I'll be bursting with lust and desire.

**HIM** Let's dispense with foreplay and have mad passionate sex.

*...give a lap dance*

**98**

**HER** Sit back and enjoy the view as I bend over and wiggle my way closer.

**HIM** Turn round, put your foot between my thighs, then lean forward and slowly unclasp your bra.

# ...do some naughty surfing

## 99

**HER** Let's take the laptop to bed and search for some exciting erotica.

**HIM** Surprise me – show me something online that secretly turns you on.

# ...spin right round

## 100

**HER** Lie down and let me try a sexy new move: a 360-degree twist.

**HIM** Give me extra thrills by bobbing up and down as well as twisting.

*...share a Basic Instinct moment*

**101**

**HER** Keep your eyes peeled as I cross and uncross my legs.

**HIM** Keep your gaze focused firmly between my legs, too – so you can see just how aroused I'm getting.

*...do some erotic bar work*

# 102

**HER** Let's have amazing stand-up sex. Give me a firm hand under my bum as I hang on to a bar above my head.

**HIM** Clasp your legs around me as I make blissful back and forth moves.

# ...take a saucy dictation

# 103

**HER** Tell me what you'd like to do in bed tonight. In detail. I'll write it all down.

**HIM** Do the hot secretary thing: take off your glasses and let your hair tumble sexily down over your shoulders...

## *...have "x" sex*

# 104

**HER** Let me do a push-up on the solid ramp of your taut body.

**HIM** You stay still while I make you gasp with hip thrusts from underneath.

# ...try it scissor style

# 105

**HER** Slide your legs up mine in a tight scissor position so your bits rub against mine.

**HIM** Wriggle your hips and angle your body so I can slip inside you.

# ...be a sex kitten

## 106

**HER** Watch me lick cream from a bowl before I slink over to be stroked by you.

**HIM** Seduce me with your feline sensuality. Cover me in cat-licks.

# ...strip for each other

## 107

**HER** Let's take turns to bare all for each other. You go first.

**HIM** Make it slow and sultry. Tease me by dropping your bra and panties into my lap.

## ...monkey around

**108**

**HER** Hang from a bar and swing towards me. Try to catch me between your legs.

**HIM** If I miss, let me drag you to the floor and seduce you properly.

*...have a hot hook up*

# 109

**HER** Let me hook my legs over your body so you can enter me at a blissful angle.

**HIM** Look me in the eye as you reach the moment of climax.

# ...flirt like strangers

## 110

**HER** Catch my eye across the room and chat me up as though we've never met before. Flirt outrageously.

**HIM** Pay me lavish compliments that get sexier as the night goes on.

*...do it chairlift style*

**111**

**HER** Support yourself on a bar, then let me sit on you like a chair so I can feel you deep inside me.

**HIM** Make me gasp with pleasure as you slide into position on my lap.

# ...be a human blanket

## 112

**HER** Drape yourself over me like a blanket as I lie back with my legs in the air.

**HIM** Let me go wild as I bump and grind my body against yours.

...*get inside each other's pants*

# 113

**HER** Let me grab you in a moment of lust and rip your pants off.

**HIM** Let me kneel at your feet and seduce you with my hot, steamy breath as I slide your panties down.

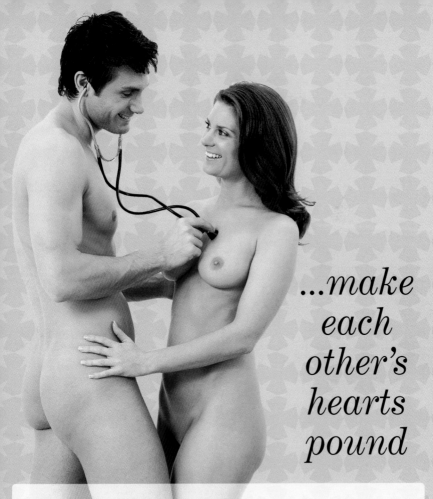

*...make
each
other's
hearts
pound*

# 114

**HER** Give me a long passionate kiss then see how fast my heart is beating.

**HIM** Let me use my stethoscope to listen to your heart... then suggest that you lie down with me for medical reasons.

# ...lend a hand

## 115

**HER** Slide your hand between my legs and make me breathless with your caresses.

**HIM** Take me firmly in hand with some smooth up-and-down strokes.

# ...try a ticklish turn-on

# 116

**HER** Give me goose bumps by brushing my skin all over.

**HIM** Tickle me and use your fingernails to graze my chest and back.

# ...pretend to be virgins

# 117

**HER** Pretend it's the first time. Let's have fun making it up as we go along.

**HIM** ...but then discover we're so good we have to keep doing repeat performances.

*...share a fruit-flavoured kiss*

# 118

**HER** Push a plump strawberry from your lips to mine as you lean in to kiss me.

**HIM** Bite into the flesh and let the juice trickle over your skin so I can lick it off.

*...enjoy erotic home dining*

# 119

**HER** Cook my favourite meal and serve it to me wearing just an apron and a chef's hat.

**HIM** Let me watch as you suck a strand of spaghetti provocatively into your mouth.

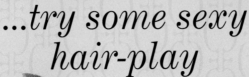

# ...try some sexy hair-play

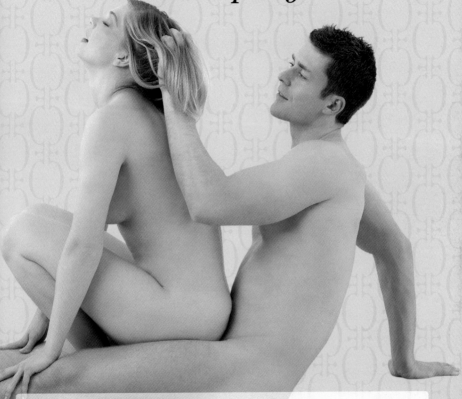

## 120

**HER** Wait until I'm super-aroused during sex then take my hair in your fist and tug.

**HIM** Give me pleasurable pain, too – dig your nails into my thighs when you're a second away from orgasm.

# ...play with pegs

Playful Dares

## 121

**HER** Give me a jolt of pleasure by gently putting pegs on my nipples.

**HIM** Let me follow up with hot and soothing tongue caresses.

*...send each other into orbit*

**122**

**HER** Take me to another planet with oral sex in the position of my choice.

**HIM** Give me a blowjob while I do a shoulderstand – for a thrilling head rush.

# ...*try sensory deprivation*

## 123

**HER** Blindfold me and wire me up to some sexy music, then ravish me.

**HIM** When it's my turn, keep me guessing with different sensations: rough and raunchy then sweet and sensual.

*...deliver some handy vibrations*

# 124

**HER** Slip a vibrator onto your finger and use it to make me tremble all over.

**HIM** Try it on me, too – give me a delicious buzz along the length of my penis.

# ...try leopard lust

## 125

**HER** Be my big sexy cat, rip off my top, then seduce me roughly while on your hands and knees.

**HIM** Bite and scratch me: don't let me have you without a fight.

...*play passionate pirate games*

# 126

**HER** Sweep me off my feet, run your rough hands all over my body, then show me your treasure.

**HIM** Play the part of my adoring sexy wench who'll do anything to please.

## ...get naughty with a scarf

# 127

**HER**: Let me slide my scarf around your neck and pull you firmly in my direction.

**HIM** When you've got me hooked, tie my wrists with the scarf and have your wicked way with me.

*...keep
her in
suspense*

# 128

**HER** Hold me tight as we invent a new stand-up sex position.

**HIM** Don't stop there – let's invent at least three more positions before we fall breathless onto the bed.

*...give a very hot greeting*

## 129

**HER** Keep your eyes closed as I greet you naughtily from behind, then slide my hands down to unbuckle your belt.

**HIM** Seduce me exactly where I'm standing. Let's make love on the spot.

# ...have sex in the office

# 130

**HER** Meet me in my office after work. I'm your go-getting boss and I know exactly what I want from you.

**HIM** Feel free to discipline me if I don't meet your every need.

# ...try Tantric worship

## 131

**HER** Let's try the Tantric ritual of lowering our bodies to the floor before we make love.

**HIM** Once we've honoured each other, let's surrender ourselves to a night of ecstatic sensuality.

# ...*pin each other down*

## 132

**HER** Overwhelm me with your strength. Pin me to the floor.

**HIM** Surprise me while I'm lying down, then straddle my body and trap my hands behind my back.

# ...squat and thrust

**133**

**HER** Pull your knees up so I can crouch between your thighs and take control.

**HIM** Let me lie back and take it easy while you take me to heaven with fast up-and-down bounces.

# ...snip your way in

## 134

**HER** Show me what lengths you'll go to to get into my panties.

**HIM** Next time, wear edible panties and I'll delight in eating them off your body.

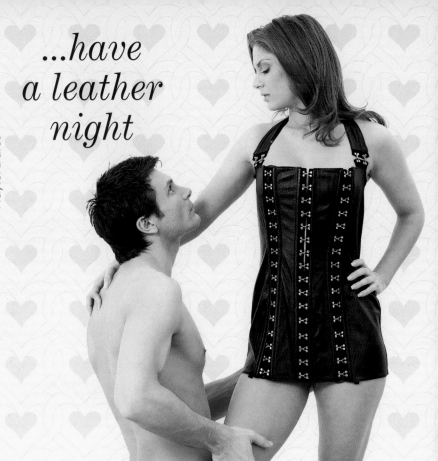

*...have a leather night*

# 135

**HER** Worship my leather-clad body – undo each catch with simmering arousal.

**HIM** First undo my leather trousers, caressing my legs as you slide them off me.

*...battle it out in bed*

# 136

**HER** Let's wait until we're feeling sex-starved then go to bed for a super-sexy playfight.

**HIM** Let's mess up the bed even more with some turbo-charged sex.

# ...try a superhero seduction

**137**

**HER** Come to my rescue – wrap me up in your cloak and thrill me with your sexy superpowers.

**HIM** Try some superhero sexual telepathy. Read my desires and fulfil them.

*...rub each other up the right way*

# 138

**HER** Get me to lie on my front so you can give me a teasing buttock massage. Make swirling patterns with your palms.

**HIM** When it's my turn, press the heels of your hands deeply into my cheeks.

*...try some stretched-out passion*

# 139

**HER** Let's have spur-of-the-moment sex. I'll hold the door jamb while you guide my stretched-out body onto yours.

**HIM** Let me run my hands over your taut, sexy curves.

*...be a cream tease*

# 140

**HER** Let me lure you into the kitchen for a naked food fight. I'll start the action with a blast of cream.

**HIM** Promise me that everything that goes on will then be licked off.

...*make a love triangle*

# 141

**HER** Hold my hips as I bend over and touch the floor with my hands. Then enter me slowly and deeply.

**HIM** Let's make it even more daring. I'll lift you into a sexy handstand.

# ...try it back-to-front

## 142

**HER** Try a slinky new sex position in which you caress my bum as I press forward over your thighs.

**HIM** Ramp up the erotic charge by talking dirty to me while I stroke you.

*...enjoy some good vibrations*

Playful Dares

**143**

**HER** Take me from zero to 60 in a second with some top-speed vibes from my favourite sex toy.

**HIM** Climb on top and drive us both crazy with the vibrator wedged between us.

# ...try raunchy push-ups

## 144

**HER** Allow me to interrupt your morning workout – I promise I'll make it so much more enjoyable.

**HIM** Thrill me with all the different x-rated push-up positions we can do.

# ...try a tantalizing come-on

# 145

**HER** Let me use all my feminine wiles to seduce you and lure you back into bed when you're supposed to be leaving.

**HIM** When you've got me in bed, lavish me with all the sex treats you know I love.

# ...fight your way into bed

## 146

**HER** Have a naked pillow-fight with me. Don't stop until we're hot and breathless.

**HIM** Do your best to get me on the floor or in bed. You haven't won until you're sitting on top of me.

# ...take the bumpy road

## 147

**HER** Put your feet on either side of my head, then slide inside me as I pull my knees up to my chest.

**HIM** Let me bump you all the way to an incredible climax.

*...get tongues wagging*

# 148

**HER** Let's give each other amazing quivers with the help of a tongue vibrator.

**HIM** Electrify me with some serious thrills: head slowly but surely down south to give me a blowjob.

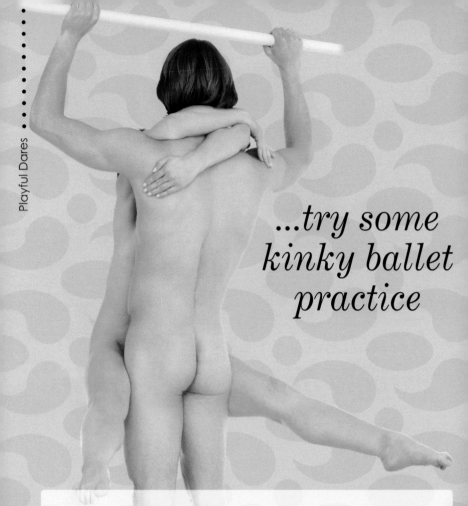

*...try some kinky ballet practice*

# 149

**HER** Be my naughty ballet teacher. Make me practice during sex.

**HIM** Take me to the peak of pleasure with your graceful body, powerful muscles, and flawless moves.

# ...make it a full circle

**150**

**HER** Make love to me missionary-style, then move around in a complete circle so I can feel you from every angle.

**HIM** Give me a playful spank on the bum when my head is level with your feet.

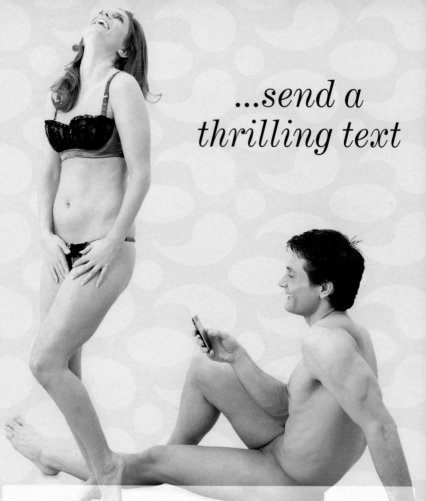

*...send a thrilling text*

# 151

**HER** Buy me the latest in sex-toy technology – a tiny vibrator that's activated by text message from your mobile.

**HIM** Slip the vibrator in your panties and let me give you a buzz.

*...indulge in the art of seduction*

**152**

**HER** Let me draw gorgeous patterns on your naked skin using a body pen.

**HIM** I'll take the pen from you and draw a curvy line that circles your breasts and belly, then snakes between your legs.

*...play master and maid*

## 153

**HER** Let me bring you breakfast in bed and help you get dressed – I'm here to serve...

**HIM** Make sure you drop something as you leave the room – then bend over very slowly to pick it up.

# ...give spoon spanks

## 154

**HER** Bend over and put your hands on your knees so I can give you a thwack with my new spanking tool.

**HIM** Lie across my lap with your bum in the air so I can return the favour.

# ...give each other a head rush

## 155

**HER** Do your best to stay in a shoulderstand while I use my finest manual skills to give you a powerful erection.

**HIM** Swap places. See if you can stay in a shoulderstand any longer than I can.

# ...explore blindly

**156**

**HER** While blindfolded, explore every inch of me with your hands, concentrating on the places that make me go "mmmm".

**HIM** Explore me, too, then keep the blindfold on while you make love to me.

# ...feast on each other's bodies

# 157

**HER** Pluck grapes one by one with your teeth. Bite into them and make the juice trickle between my legs.

**HIM** Make a row of grapes from my chest to my pubes. Start eating from the top...

## ...do a sitting 69

# 158

**HER** Let's get into a lying down 69 with my legs around your head. Then hug me tight and slowly sit up.

**HIM** Let's make some quick tongue moves before we collapse on the bed.

# ...play the hat game

## 159

**HER** Let's write down all our sexual fantasies on strips of paper. Each night we pull one out of a hat and act it out.

**HIM** Go deep into your erotic imagination – thrill me with your suggestions.

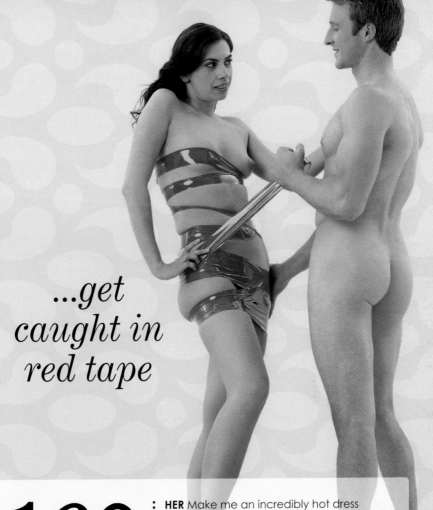

*...get caught in red tape*

**160**

**HER** Make me an incredibly hot dress by winding a reel of red bondage tape around my body.

**HIM** When it's my turn you can make me some kinky black shorts.

# ...be his sexy Santa

## 161

**HER** Let me take you back to bed for a saucy start to Christmas Day.

**HIM** Present yourself in your sexiest festive undies so I can have the pleasure of unwrapping you.

# ...spend the night down under

## 162

**HER** Make me gasp and moan with your best oral sex techniques – don't stop until I have a mind-blowing orgasm.

**HIM** When you've recovered, slide down my body and take me in your hot mouth.

# ...give a cheeky love bite

## 163

**HER** Make me gasp with pleasure by sucking hard and making a mark that I can secretly cherish.

**HIM** Make your mark on me, too – on the erogenous zone of your choice.

*...play hard to get*

# 164

**HER** Try to seduce me from a distance as I hold you at arm's length.

**HIM** Present me with a tough challenge. Even when you're burning with desire, don't let me know about it.

# ...bite the cherry

# 165

**HER** Tempt me with delicious bite-sized morsels – cherries, grapes, chocolates – as I lounge in bed.

**HIM** Take the cherry between your teeth then sit up and push it into my mouth.

*...play strip poker*

**166**

**HER** Let's close the curtains and settle in for a night of steamy poker.

**HIM** Play recklessly so I can feast my eyes on your half-naked body.

*...share
Turkish
delights*

# 167

**HER** Let's have a night of Eastern eroticism, starting with a steamy bath and a massage.

**HIM** ...followed by a topless belly dance in which you drive me crazy with your amazing hip moves.

# ...play ball games

## 168

**HER** Make me scream with delight by grabbing me when I'm on my exercise ball.

**HIM** Open your legs and let's have fun trying to have sex. Let's try a wobbly wheelbarrow position.

*...use thigh power*

# 169

**HER** Kneel down, then lean back on your elbows so I can hop on top. Bounce me fast on your thighs.

**HIM** Hold on tight for the ride, and squeeze me hard between your legs.

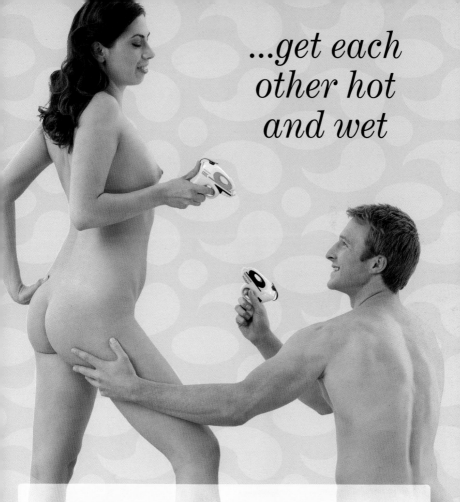

...get each
other hot
and wet

**170**

**HER** Let's arm ourselves with water pistols and have a naked water fight.

**HIM** Fill the pistols with hot water and massage oil. When the fight's over let's slip and slide all over each other.

*...play bride and groom*

**171**

**HER** Treat me like your virginal bride – slide the veil from my hair, kiss me passionately, and carry me to bed.

**HIM** Let me roll your stockings down then slowly kiss my way up your legs.

...be a
*flirty flight
attendant*

# 172

**HER** Let me slide my leg up yours and indulge all your flight attendant fantasies.

**HIM** Welcome me on board in your sexiest voice and give me a personal invitation to join the mile-high club.

...*get on a roll*

Playful Dares

# 173

**HER** Throw me on to the bed with the force of your passion. Jump on top and roll my body backward.

**HIM** Hook your leg over my shoulder for deep, intense sensations.

# ...try a sexy new slant

## 174

**HER** Lie across my body crossways then relish the erotic friction as you push yourself between my tightly closed thighs.

**HIM** Let me smooth massage oil onto your thighs first for a breathtaking entrance.

# ...get frisky under cover

**175**

**HER** Pull a big blanket around us in a semi-public place and touch me inappropriately.

**HIM** Keep a normal conversation going as I slide my hand between your legs.

# ...give a tiger massage

## 176

**HER** Make your hands into big sexy tiger paws then slowly claw your way down my back and bum.

**HIM** Be a predatory tigress. Turn on me – claw and bite me back.

# ...*put your foot where it shouldn't be*

**177**

**HER** Turn me on by slipping your toes between my legs and wiggling them. Try it under a restaurant table.

**HIM** Drive me crazy in the same way. Let's try to keep a normal conversation going.

*...try sweet distraction*

# 178

**HER** Use every weapon in your erotic armory to lure me away from my book.

**HIM** Make me try harder and harder to seduce you, before you finally turn over and wrap your arms and legs around me.

# ...make each other's spines tingle

## 179

**HER** Pretend I'm your favourite ice cream – draw a line along my spine with the tip of your tongue.

**HIM** When it's my turn, lick me to the nape of my neck then whisper something dirty.

*...have a very personal check-up*

# 180

**HER** Be my sexy personal doctor. Take my pulse, then examine me from head to toe as I lie naked on the bed.

**HIM** Make me drop all my professional boundaries and pounce on you.

# ...say it with a feather

# 181

**HER** Take some body paint and a feather pen and write an x-rated message across my breasts.

**HIM** Give me whole-body tingles by wafting the fluffy part of the feather all over me.

# ...make the earth move

## 182

**HER** Thrill me during sitting-down sex by lifting me up in the air.

**HIM** Let's make gorgeous mid-air movements and then come down to earth with a bump for the climax.

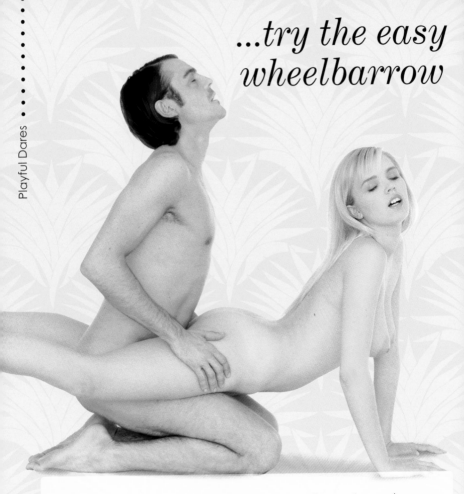

## ...try the easy wheelbarrow

# 183

**HER** Part my legs, pull me onto your lap, and make me gasp with a thrilling entry.

**HIM** Fall forward onto the bed so that I can lie on top of you and move freely for the grand finale.

*...try the tricky wheelbarrow*

# 184

**HER** Let's try some daring sexual athletics – I'll get into a bridge position, then you pick me up and guide me onto you.

**HIM** Start with some heavy smooching so we're both primed and ready for action.

*sexy*
**DARES**

*...give double the pleasure*

# 185

**HER** Target two of my favourite places by sitting behind me: tweak my nipples and caress my clitoris.

**HIM** Make me delirious by licking me from behind while stroking my penis.

*...put on an erotic show*

# 186

**HER** Moan appreciatively as I strike some incredibly erotic poses around the bedroom.

**HIM** Reveal your most exhibitionist side – leave nothing to my imagination.

*...give an open invitation*

# 187

**HER** Make me bite my lip with pleasure as you go down on me.

**HIM** Let me give you an earth-shattering orgasm followed by swift penetration.

*...reach dizzying heights of passion*

# 188

**HER** Take me higher than you've ever taken me before: let me straddle your shoulders while you lick me.

**HIM** Slide down so your thighs are around my waist. Let me take you against the wall.

*...devote yourself to the job*

# 189

**HER** Give yourself up to pleasuring me with your lips, and tongue. Bury your face in me.

**HIM** When it's my turn, push me on to a chair then let me sit back and bask in bliss.

*...make it fast and urgent*

**190**

**HER** Let's have a wild two-minute quickie. Take me from behind in doggie position.

**HIM** Lift your bum high in the air and lean forward on your elbows so I can penetrate you deeply.

# ...have sex on the edge

# 191

**HER** Push me over the edge of the bed as you make love to me. Give me a dizzying rush of blood to my head.

**HIM** Let's make it so passionate that we go over the edge and land on the floor.

*...dive in the deep end*

**192**

**HER** Gently explore my depths while I kneel on a chair and push my bum in the air.

**HIM** Let me slide slowly inside you, then stay still for a moment of peak erotic intensity.

# ...take some toys to bed

# 193

**HER** Let's get the sex toys out – I'll tell you which one's my favourite and why.

**HIM** Roll me over and sit astride me while you put a vibrating ring on my penis. Now climb on board.

# ...use two hands instead of one

**194**

**HER** Give me an amazingly intense orgasm by pressing and stroking my G-spot while I caress my clitoris.

**HIM** Let me follow closely behind by making love to you in spoons position.

# ...give a massage that turns naughty

## 195

**HER** Let me brush my nipples against your lips as I give you a slippery oil massage.

**HIM** Slide all the way down until we're in a sizzlingly hot 69 position.

# ...have a
# red-hot reunion

## 196

**HER** Demand I join you in bed after we've been apart. Wink at me, then make me a filthy proposition.

**HIM** Wear your hottest lingerie so I can have fun taking it off.

# ...make the pleasure mutual

## 197

**HER** Make me explode by using your tongue and fingers on me at the same time.

**HIM** Slide your lips around my shaft in a fast rhythm that I can't resist.

*...try some sexploration*

**198**

**HER** Trail your fingertips along my thighs, circle my clitoris, then slip your fingers inside me to caress my G-spot.

**HIM** Stroke my shaft, tickle my balls, then smooth your fingers back to find my G-spot.

*...do it
with
gloves on*

# 199

**HER** Let me give you a sensual seduction. Guide my gloved hands to the places you most want to be touched.

**HIM** Sit on top of me and rake your silky fingers all over me.

# ...unwind with oral

## 200

**HER** Take me to another dimension with leisurely oral sex at the end of the day.

**HIM** Let me lie back and relax while you seduce me with sensual tongue twirls.

*...enjoy a full-on crush*

# 201

**HER** Crush my legs against my breasts – let me feel the sexy weight of your body on top of mine.

**HIM** Maximize the intensity by gazing into my eyes and gasping my name.

# ...be rude with food

## 202

**HER** Give me a naughty look as you suggestively tip an oyster into your mouth or bite into a ripe fig.

**HIM** Tease me by sliding your lips down a banana as far as you can.

...*try the chair challenge*

# 203

**HER** Let's discover all the different ways we can have sex on a chair.

**HIM** Let's finish with an erotic classic: me sitting on the chair and you on my lap in a passionate cuddle.

# ...see who gets there first

## 204

**HER** Let's lick each other in an intoxicating rhythm and see who comes first.

**HIM** Let's synchronize our moves and aim for a mind-blowing simultaneous orgasm.

*...have wanton wall sex*

# 205

**HER** Tell me how much you want me, then pick me up, and press me hard against the nearest wall.

**HIM** Twine your arms around my neck and devour me with a kiss.

# ...*spring-load your lust*

## 206

**HER** Let me push off against your chest in lust-fuelled passion.

**HIM** Wiggle your bum tightly into my lap for a close fit that makes me throb.

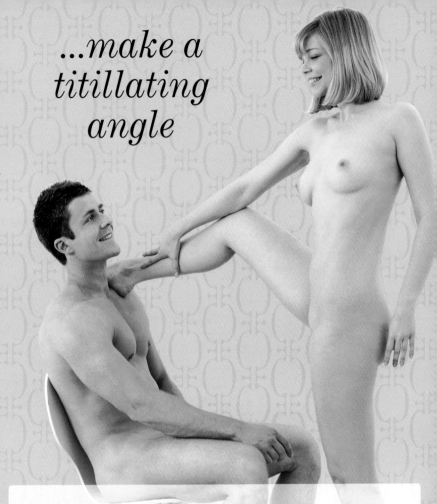

## ...make a titillating angle

**207**

**HER** Sit patiently while I inflame you with burning hot poses.

**HIM** When I can't take it any more, straddle me and guide me deeply inside you.

*...flip your love*

**208**

**HER** Enjoy the view as I move from a sexy forward straddle to an x-rated backbend across your lap.

**HIM** Thrill me with more sexual acrobatics, then have wild sex with me.

*...go joy-riding*

# 209

**HER** Stroke and tweak my nipples while I ride my way to an explosive on-top orgasm.

**HIM** Grind your pelvis in a fast back-and-forth rhythm so I can climax with you.

# ...hand deliver an orgasm

## 210

**HER** Take me to heaven with your thumb circling on my clitoris and your other hand stroking my G-spot.

**HIM** Lace your oiled fingers around my penis and glide them smoothly up and down.

*...get a kick out of watching*

# 211

**HER** Turn me on by sliding your hands over me as we watch in the mirror.

**HIM** Let's make it even hotter – bend over so I can take you from behind. Meet my gaze in the mirror.

# ...take a trip down south

## 212

**HER** Slide underneath me when I'm on all fours – tease me with your tongue.

**HIM** Make me shiver with anticipation – pause at my navel before heading to your final destination.

*...do the*
*"body slide"*

**213**

**HER** Make me purr with pleasure by sliding your well-oiled body slowly along the full length of mine.

**HIM** Open your legs as I glide up your body so I can penetrate you at the last moment.

# ...give a repeat performance

## 214

**HER** Kneel astride me so I can take you in hand and make you hard all over again.

**HIM** When I'm rigid with arousal push me onto my back and sit firmly on top of me for round two.

# ...be a
# *sexual predator*

## 215

**HER** Thrill me with your animal magnetism – jump on top and ravish me with a hungry look in your eye.

**HIM** Push your hips up high and open your legs to welcome me.

# ...give the sexiest gift

## 216

**HER** Wrap yourself in sexy black bondage tape and give yourself to me as a present.

**HIM** Twine red ribbons around your body. Ask me to undo your bows.

*...ramp it up*

# 217

**HER** Slide a sex ramp underneath me so I'm at the perfect angle to take you in deeply.

**HIM** Tell me in a breathless whisper how you want me to move: "faster", "slower" – or just say "ohhhhhhhhh".

*...steam me up with your breath*

**218**

**HER** Lie with your head on my lap and steam me up by slowly exhaling so the heat spreads through my panties.

**HIM** Hover your lips over the tip of my penis and drive me crazy with just your breath.

*...be a voyeur*

# 219

**HER** Let me enjoy some hot fantasies as I watch you in the shower.

**HIM** Let me watch you caress your naked body in front of the mirror. Pretend you're alone – get carried away.

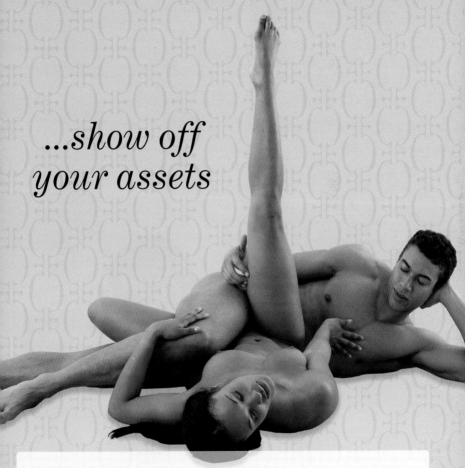

*...show off your assets*

**220**

**HER** Moan appreciatively as I stretch my leg in the air during sex. Trail your fingers along my inner thigh.

**HIM** Go a step further: wear sexy black stockings and heels.

# ...make a
# late entrance

## 221

**HER** Come to bed late and wake me up with your gorgeous body slinking up mine.

**HIM** Make sure you don't wake up completely – let me enter you slowly for sleepy and sensual passion.

# ...share bites and nibbles

## 222

**HER** Make me simmer with lust as you graze my bum with your teeth.

**HIM** Cover me with bites of different shapes and sizes – everything from teasing nips to succulent love bites.

*...be naughty on an exercise ball*

**223**

**HER** Bring a smile to my face – go down on me during my exercise ball workout.

**HIM** Let's swap places so you can bounce me to an uncontrollable orgasm using your hands and mouth.

*...put on a peep show*

# 224

**HER** Watch while I undress to my bra and panties and tease you mercilessly. Show how much you want me with your eyes.

**HIM** Be a brazen exhibitionist. Give me gorgeous glimpses of your breasts.

# ...make an erotic movie

## 225

**HER** Worship me with the camera. Film me taking my clothes off and dancing naked for you.

**HIM** Lose all your inhibitions – show me your inner diva as I film you.

# ...try some sizzling moves

**226**

**HER** Let me kick start your excitement by dressing up and grinding my hips in sexy circles. You can thank me in bed.

**HIM** Do my favourite move – bend over with your legs straight, then glance back at me.

*...make it electrifying*

**227**

**HER** Make me writhe with pleasure – slide a pebble-shaped vibrator between my legs and turn it up to the max.

**HIM** Let me add to your pleasure with some smooth thrusts from behind.

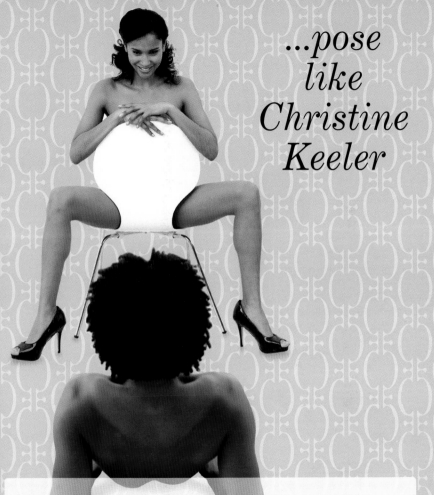

*...pose like Christine Keeler*

**228**

**HER** Let me seduce you with a series of stunning sitting-down poses. At the end I'll stand up and strut towards you.

**HIM** Let me snap some gorgeous pics for our private erotic album.

# ...pounce, push, and pull

## 229

**HER** Have a sexy tussle with me – pounce on me and push me to the floor. I'll pull you in with my legs around your body.

**HIM** As the passion mounts, pull your knees up and put your feet on my chest.

# ...cover all bases

**230**

**HER** Make me melt in your arms by tweaking my nipples and caressing my clitoris at the same time.

**HIM** Cover my bases with your fingers on my penis and your lips caressing my balls.

*...give a taste
of things to
come*

**231**

**HER** Let me give you a preview of tonight's action by ripping open your flies and taking you in my mouth.

**HIM** After a thrilling 10 seconds, zip me back up and promise to continue later.

# ...share your lollipop

**232**

**HER** Flirt provocatively with me – ask if you can suck my lollipop.

**HIM** Pull me close and circle your tongue naughtily around the lollipop before you hand it over.

# ...try the "rowing boat"

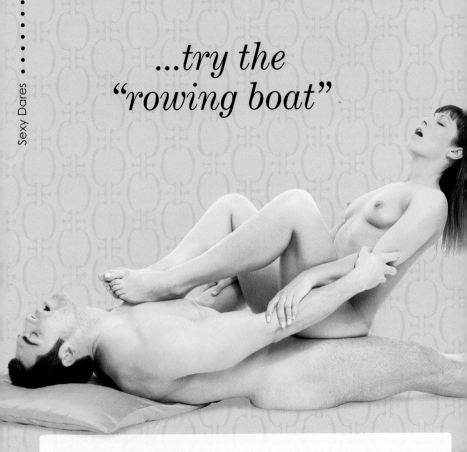

## 233

**HER** Let me climb on board your boat and row you hard.

**HIM** Rub oil into your body so you slip gloriously back and forth on me.

*...do it on a
sex chair*

# 234

**HER** Slide underneath my chair so I can have the joy of impaling myself on your waiting erection.

**HIM** Once you're in position turn us both to liquid with super-fast bounces.

*...share some
naughty
memories*

**235**

**HER** Turn me on by describing the first time
we had sex together – remind me of the
intimate details.

**HIM** Tell me a favourite erotic memory from
our sex life – make it explicit.

## ...dress Burlesque for the night

**236**

**HER** Let me show off my hour-glass figure in a sexy Burlesque corset.

**HIM** Go a step further: wear elbow-length satin gloves, a top hat, and nipple tassels. Strip for me.

*...don't take no for an answer*

**237**

**HER** Don't try to resist. I'm pulling your clothes off and dragging you to bed.

**HIM** Strip me naked, then sit astride me, and pin my arms above my head. Help yourself to me.

# ...try a 69 for the feet

# 238

**HER** Lie top-to-tail with me so we can give each other a sensational toe massage by mouth. Lick, suck, and nibble.

**HIM** Up my pleasure by enclosing my erection tightly between your thighs.

*...get sticky together*

**239**

**HER** Watch while I drizzle honey over my breasts, then when you can't take any more, fall to your knees and start licking.

**HIM** Pour honey on me, too, so we can enjoy sweet, sticky friction as we make love.

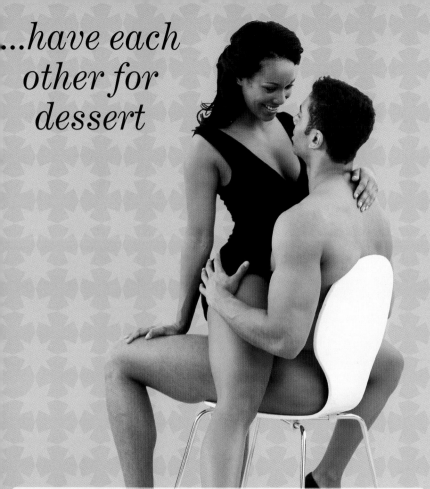

# ...have each other for dessert

## 240

**HER** Pull me onto your lap after we've had a delicious dinner. Let's skip dessert and feast on each other.

**HIM** Hitch your dress up and press your body tight against mine.

## ...indulge in self-pleasure

**241**

**HER** Let's get an erotic high from watching each other masturbate.

**HIM** Let's match our arousal levels so we can hit the peak together. Look into my eyes as you climax.

*...try deep throat*

**242**

**HER** Let's try the famous oral sex trick: slide your penis gently into my mouth as I lie with my head off the edge of the bed.

**HIM** Take as much of me in as you can while I stroke your breasts.

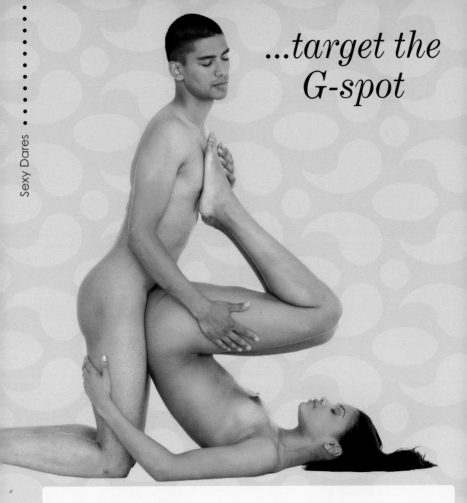

# ...target the G-spot

## 243

**HER** Give me sensational shudders by plunging into me and targeting my G-spot with the head of your penis.

**HIM** Let me know when I've hit the spot with an "ahhhh" or an "ohhhh".

## ...be a fiery red head

# 244

**HER** Slide your hands hungrily up and down my body as I surprise you with my sexy new red bob.

**HIM** Indulge all my fantasies about red heads – be brazen and wicked.

*...offer outdoor oral*

# 245

**HER** Go down on me when we're outdoors. Press me against a tree or a wall and make it super-fast.

**HIM** Get off on the wicked frisson of having a semi-public orgasm.

*...have a reviving sex break*

# 246

**HER** Let me slink up from behind in my undies. Close your eyes while I distract you with a penetrating back rub.

**HIM** Close the lid of my computer and sit on my lap for a very sexy work break.

# ...get in a
# tight squeeze

## 247

**HER** Come over all macho and dominant. Throw my legs over your shoulders and make me feel the weight of your lust.

**HIM** Relax your whole body so I can sink blissfully into you.

# ...make it multiple

## 248

**HER** See if you can give me multiple orgasms with your twisting and twining tongue skills.

**HIM** Hold on tight as I make you bounce off the walls with my fingers, too.

# ...get down on the ranch

## 249

**HER** Adopt a new erotic persona: be my strong and sexy ranch boy. Don't speak, just take me to bed.

**HIM** Play a sexy, sultry role, too. Run your hands lingeringly over my biceps and chest.

*...have an oil spill*

**250**

**HER**: "Spill" some massage oil on me – make me shiny, slick, and slippery.

**HIM** Moan with pleasure as I slide and glide my hands all over your breasts and nipples.

*...undress by stealth*

# 251

**HER** Make me swoon with a lingering kiss that's so hot I don't notice how you're slipping my skirt over my hips.

**HIM** Focus on kissing me passionately. Leave the rest to me.

# ...try the wet T-shirt trick

**252**

**HER** Go wide-eyed with lust as I slip onto your lap in a tight wet T-shirt that perfectly outlines my bare breasts.

**HIM** Let me watch as you pull your T-shirt off and throw it teasingly over your shoulder.

# ...do it the Thai way

## 253

**HER** Start the evening with a Thai soapsud massage. Cover me in lather and slide your hands all over me.

**HIM** Give me a Thai oil massage – bend and press me until I'm supple and pliant.

# ...play cheeky chess

## 254

**HER** Play naked chess with me – the winner gets to call the shots in bed.

**HIM** Make me simmer with lust as you stretch languorously across the board to move your pieces.

# ...have the breast fun ever

## 255

**HER** Devote yourself to breast caresses. Plant featherlight kisses around each breast, then zone in on my nipples with your lips.

**HIM** Test my nipple sensitivity, too – try licking and tweaking.

*...take it to the bridge*

**256**

**HER** Kneel down and take me in a wide-open bridge position.

**HIM** Lift your pelvis really high then move in slow sexy undulations that take me straight to paradise.

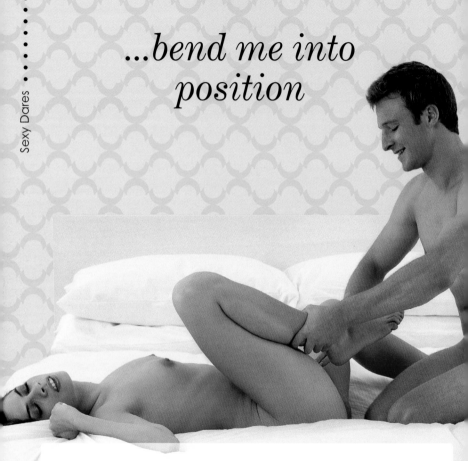

*...bend me into position*

## 257

**HER** Bend my legs and push them into my chest – then climb smoothly on top.

**HIM** Try lots of different sex positions with me – let me bend you into the shape I want.

# ...*work your way up*

## 258

**HER** Cover me with long, soft kisses, starting with my toes and working your way slowly up my body.

**HIM** Let me pause at the places that make you tremble with pleasure.

# ...give a Tantric breast massage

## 259

**HER** Pull me onto your lap in the "Yab Yum" position then smooth your open hands incredibly slowly over my breasts.

**HIM** Slide forward and take me inside you for some internal joy, too.

# ....dress to undress

## 260

**HER** Take me out to dinner. I'll put on my sexiest dress and you can fantasize about watching me take it off later.

**HIM** Indulge me the moment we get home. Give me the most tantalizing views.

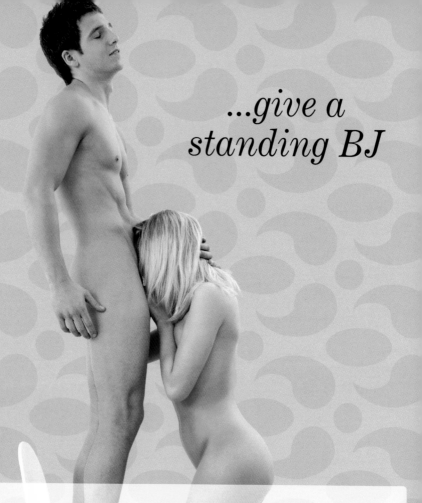

## ...give a standing BJ

## 261

**HER** Stand on a chair so I can take you in my mouth with ease. Relish the naughty novelty of a new position.

**HIM** Make me weak-kneed and light-headed with arousal.

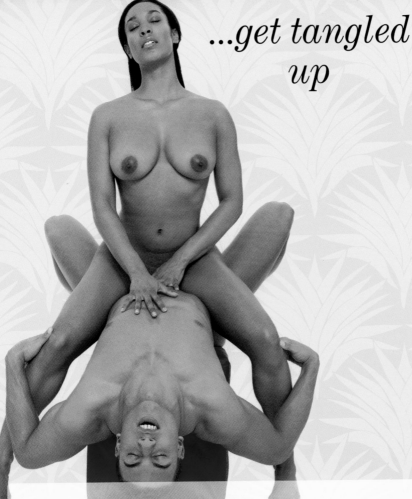

# ...get tangled up

## 262

**HER** Let's get into an intimate tangle – bend backwards with your heels against your bum while I sit astride your hot body.

**HIM** Bounce up and down on me. Rake my chest with your fingers.

# ...be a hair tease

## 263

**HER** Close your eyes and let me treat you to some deliciously ticklish sensations.

**HIM** Slide down my body and twine your long hair around my erection. Make me gasp by pulling away.

*...flash!*

**264**

**HER** Let me indulge my secret fantasy to flash in public.

**HIM** Open your coat wide and bare all. Or try a different kind of flash: bend over while wearing a short skirt and a tiny thong.

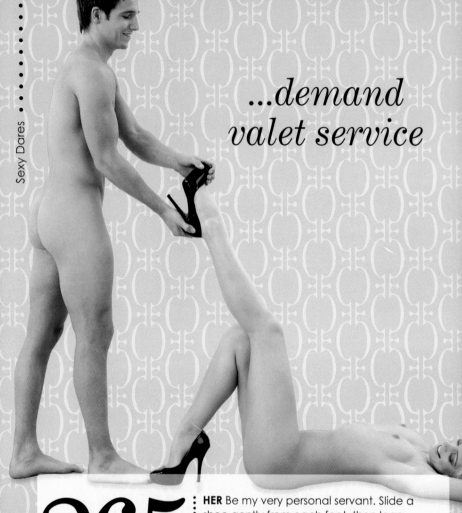

*...demand
valet service*

**265**

**HER** Be my very personal servant. Slide a
shoe gently from each foot, then lean
forward to kiss my toes.

**HIM** Point each leg in the air while arching
your back and pushing your breasts out.

# ...be my gym instructor

**266**

**HER** Help me out with my stretches – lie on top of me and force my feet over my head.

**HIM** Stand up – your next exercise is to bend over and touch your toes while I stand behind you.

# ...be a naughty tea lady

## 267

**HER** Let me seduce you with afternoon tea in bed – served in just a skimpy apron and a pair of heels.

**HIM** Take the empty tray out so I can watch your bare bum as you walk away.

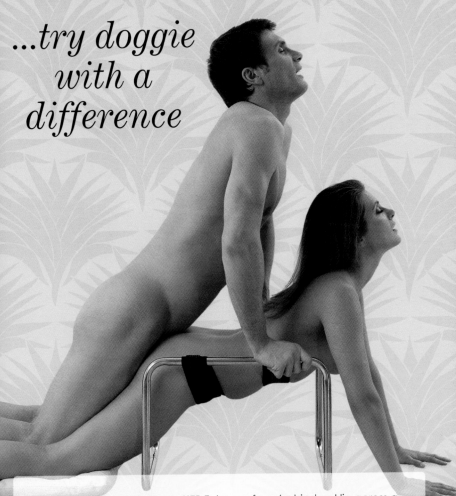

## ...try doggie with a difference

# 268

**HER** Take me from behind as I lie across a sex chair. Let me abandon myself to the rapture of weightless sex.

**HIM** Let your body spring back to meet mine after each thrust.

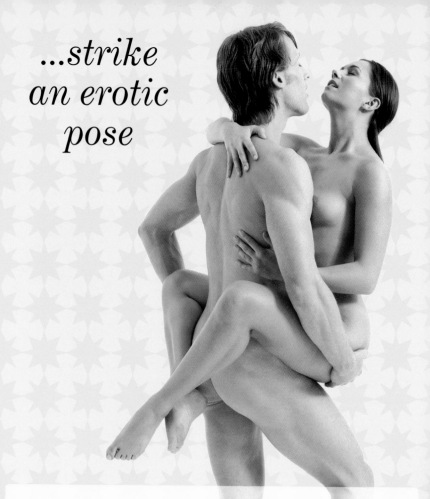

# ...strike an erotic pose

# 269

**HER** Set a camera on auto-timer so we can take an erotic snap of ourselves in a picture-perfect sex position.

**HIM** Even better, let's video ourselves as we get swept away by passion.

*...play with a rabbit*

# 270

**HER** Give me body-shaking pleasure by holding a rabbit vibrator against my clitoris while you enter me from behind.

**HIM** Thrill me with your climactic moans of pure joy.

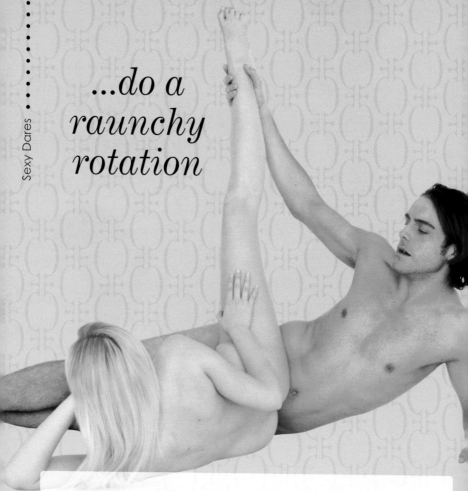

*...do a raunchy rotation*

# 271

**HER** Let's start off with some sensual spoon position sex. Then I'll lean forward and raise my leg in the air for some divine sensations.

**HIM** Rotate some more so you're lying on your back with both legs in the air.

*...pop to the bathroom at a party*

# 272

**HER** Let's slip off for a very naughty liaison in the bathroom.

**HIM** Let me take you passionately against the wall, sitting on the toilet, and bending over in front of the basin.

# ...press your cheeks together

## 273

**HER** Lie down with me – snuggle your bum up to mine and feel the sexual tension start to grow.

**HIM** When I'm bursting at the seams with desire, let's try to have sex in this position.

# ...discover a new way to climax

## 274

**HER** Find a new way of pleasuring me – slide your foot between my legs and wiggle your toes against my clitoris.

**HIM** Let me slip my toe inside you as you caress yourself by hand.

*...be a sexy double act*

**275**

**HER** Let's do some sexy teamwork – we both wrap our arms around each other and lick feverishly.

**HIM** Thrill me with more sexy feats we can include in our double act.

# ...spoon feed each other

## 276

**HER** Bring my favourite ice cream to bed. Feed me one sensual spoonful at a time.

**HIM** Give me an erotic shiver by going down on me when your mouth is still cold from the ice cream.

# ...thrill him with heels

**277**

**HER** Be on your best behaviour – I'm wearing heels to bed and I'll use them to control you.

**HIM** Press the spikes into me so I can feel that hot mix of pleasure and pain.

*...try a mid-sex spank*

# 278

**HER** Cup your hand and take me by surprise with a firm spank on my bum as you're making love to me.

**HIM** Moan softly as I rub your bum better with gentle circling of my palm.

# ...do the slowest striptease

## 279

**HER** Be my adoring audience as I slowly strip for you. Wait until the end before pouncing.

**HIM** Give me the sexiest view possible: rest your foot by me and slowly smooth your stockings over your thighs.

*...unzip a sexy package*

**280**

**HER** Come to bed in some hot underwear: a posing pouch, a thong, or some bum-hugging boxers.

**HIM** Thrill me with your undies, too. Let's unwrap each other at the same time.

*...take lap dancing to the next level*

# 281

**HER** Let me drive you insane by moving my hips in slow figures of eight while standing astride your lap.

**HIM** Keep swirling your hips as you do a deep squat that brushes against my thighs.

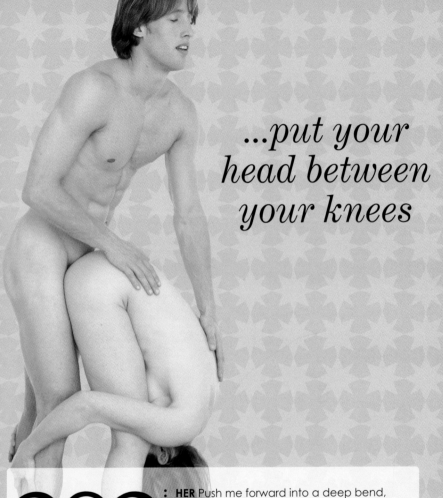

## ...put your head between your knees

**282**

**HER** Push me forward into a deep bend, then make me gasp with some gorgeously penetrating in-and-out strokes.

**HIM** Let's make it a slow build up to an explosive climax.

# ...try a slow and leisurely 69

## 283

**HER** Lie on your side and rest your head on my thigh. Now precision-target my hotspots and give me a slow and luscious licking.

**HIM** Swirl your tongue on the head of my penis as if you've got all day.

*...try weightless sex*

**284**

**HER** Feel the intense joy of me swinging on and off you as I hang on to a bar above my head.

**HIM** Let me grab your thighs and speed up your moves.

# ...*seduce each other with cream*

# 285

**HER** Make my breasts tingle by spraying chilled cream on them. Seduce me by licking it all off.

**HIM** Spray the tip of my penis with cream and then enclose it softly in your mouth.

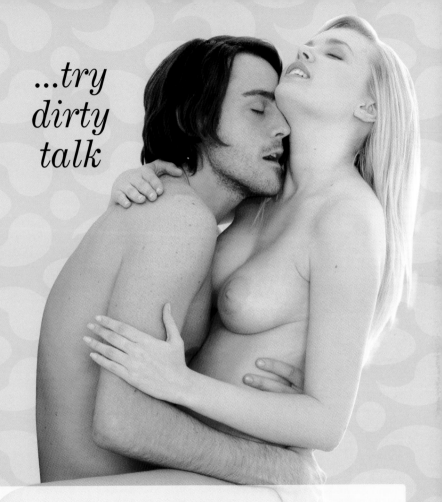

*...try dirty talk*

# 286

**HER** Make me bounce off the walls by giving an x-rated description of what you want to do to me.

**HIM** Be just as filthy back. Keep the conversation going until we climax.

*...give each other the hot and cold treatment*

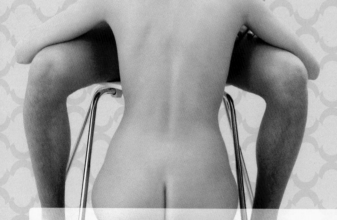

# 287

**HER** Go down on me after you've sucked an ice cube. Then thaw me out by licking me after a mouthful of hot tea.

**HIM** Give me a cool, zingy feeling by sucking a mint during a blowjob.

# ...do it in a cubicle

## 288

**HER** Sneak into my changing room/toilet cubicle for a very naughty quickie when no one's around.

**HIM** Help yourself to me as I brace myself against the wall.

*...do it rodeo style*

# 289

**HER** Have fast, untamed sex with me as I get down on my knees and elbows.

**HIM** Buck, writhe, and swerve while I do my best to contain you.

# ...set up a sexy studio

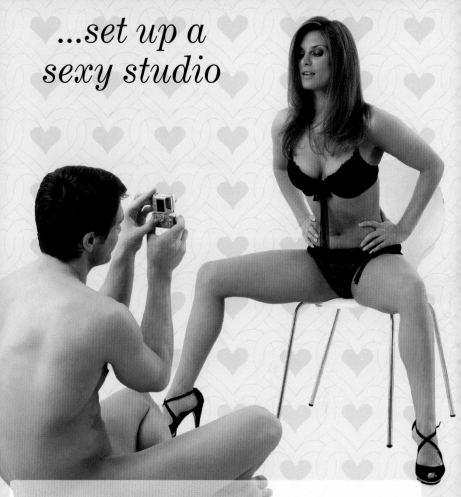

## 290

**HER** Turn the bedroom into a studio and invite me in for a casting session.

**HIM** Impress me with your hottest moves – flirt shamelessly with the camera. Force me to behave unprofessionally.

# *kinky* DARES

*...try an erotic trapeze act*

**291**

**HER** Amaze me with your trapeze skills and your tongue skillls at the same time.

**HIM** Later, in bed, tell me in an awed voice how incredible that was.

*...trap him with your legs*

**292**

**HER** Let me wrap my legs around your waist and trap you by crossing my ankles behind your back.

**HIM** Let me take advantage with a sudden and piercing penetration.

*...threaten*
*erotic*
*punishment*

**293**

**HER** Lie at my feet as I brandish my whip. Expect to be punished if you don't please me.

**HIM** Tease me by trailing your whip softly along my body.

# ...get raunchy on the staircase

## 294

**HER** Let's have raunchy stair sex – hold me in place on your lap while I do a dramatic forward lean.

**HIM** Let me grab your hips and move you on and off me.

*...do a
kinky
handstand*

# 295

**HER** Catch my legs as I do a naked handstand. Admire me from a new and naughty angle.

**HIM** Give me a speedy blowjob as I do a handstand against the wall.

# ...be daring with a dildo

**296**

**HER** Kiss, stroke, and arouse me, then slip a glass dildo gently inside me as I open my legs wide.

**HIM** Add a touch of kinkiness by getting into a shoulderstand and doing the splits.

# ...thrill her with your bar skills

## 297

**HER** Show off your gorgeous muscles and fit sexy body with some amazing bar work.

**HIM** While I'm hanging from the bar tease me with your tongue – flick the tip cheekily between my buttocks.

# ...get him in a hot headlock

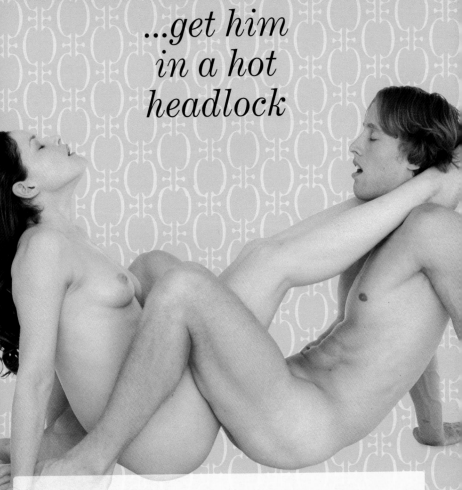

## 298

**HER** Let's start with some sensual sitting-down sex, then I'll make it naughtier by holding you in place with my feet.

**HIM** Cross your ankles behind my head and pull me towards you.

# ...take the driving seat

## 299

**HER** Let me hang on to your legs as I bump and grind my way to an intense orgasm.

**HIM** Lie back on me afterwards so I can run my hands over your belly and breasts, before rolling you onto your front.

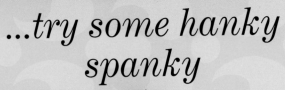

# ...try some hanky spanky

## 300

**HER** Undress me, then tell me to bend over your lap in your sternest voice.

**HIM** Let me make you gasp with a firm thwack to your bum.

# ...feel your way in

## 301

**HER** Let's explore each other's body with a blindfold on. Use your lips, tongue, fingers, and toes to discover every part of me.

**HIM** As we get turned on let's grope our way into a sex position that feels amazing.

# ...take the back route

## 302

**HER** Make me weak with pleasure by swirling and twirling your tongue in a line that starts at my vagina and goes back.

**HIM** Do the same thrilling detour next time you're giving me a blowjob.

# ...bind her to the seat

# 303

**HER** Use bondage tape to trap me on my seat. Don't release me until you've finished with me.

**HIM** Let me make you squirm with pleasure by kissing my way up your thighs.

# ...do it with cuffs on

## 304

**HER** Playfully catch my legs and snap a pair of ankle cuffs on me. Now arrange me in your favourite position.

**HIM** Make me wear the cuffs next time. Take advantage by sitting astride me.

# ...take it step by step

## 305

**HER** Drop your trousers and push my legs apart as I'm sitting on the stairs. Lean in for a deliciously tight fit.

**HIM** Let's work our way up the stairs, then fall into bed for the climax.

# ...try lotus position lust

## 306

**HER** Admire my supple body as I stretch my legs provocatively in the air and fold them smoothly into lotus position.

**HIM** Let me show the force of my appreciation by jumping on top of you.

# ...get him in your grip

# 307

**HER** Offer me your hand so I can grip you hard as I lean back to find the perfect angle for G-spot bliss.

**HIM** Throw your head back and push your chest out as you reach a peak of pleasure.

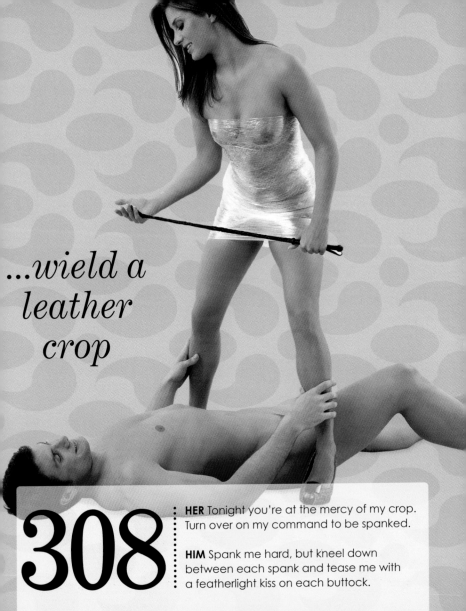

*...wield a leather crop*

# 308

**HER** Tonight you're at the mercy of my crop. Turn over on my command to be spanked.

**HIM** Spank me hard, but kneel down between each spank and tease me with a featherlight kiss on each buttock.

*...make it a
tight fit*

# 309

**HER** Push my legs together, bind my ankles, then lift my legs in the air.

**HIM** Savour the intense friction as I curl my body around yours and push myself tightly into you.

...have a sex change

# 310

**HER** Give me a kinky turn-on by going girly for the night – dress up in one of my tops and show me your feminine side.

**HIM** Dress in my clothes for a sexy boyish look – now grab me for a snog.

*...treat each other like royalty*

# 311

**HER** Bend over backwards to make me comfortable as I get into a sexy on-top position. Dedicate yourself to my pleasure.

**HIM** Repay me by treating me like a king – begin with a long erotic massage.

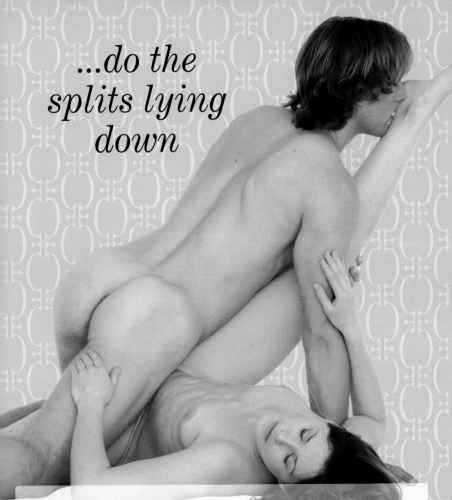

# ...do the splits lying down

## 312

**HER** Watch as I lie on the bed and open my legs in an awe-inspiringly wide "V".

**HIM** Stay in position as I kiss you from your inner thigh to your heel, and then smoothly enter you.

# ...be a naughty schoolgirl

Kinky Dares

# 313

**HER** Invite me for a smooching session behind the bikesheds as I flirt with you in my schoolgirl outfit.

**HIM** Lift your skirt to give me a titillating glimpse of your bare bum.

## ...try a bondage classic

# 314

**HER** Let's have a kinky bondage night. I'll be the dom and you be the sub.

**HIM** Order me to lie on my stomach, then tie my ankles to my wrists in a classic "hogtie" and spank me.

*...try a spanking session*

**315**

**HER** Find out how I like to be spanked: try light pats and firm whacks. Try one side of my bum and then across the middle.

**HIM** Change positions, too. Bend forward and touch your toes.

# ...let ladies come first

**316**

**HER** Kiss me passionately while I slip a vibrator inside my panties.

**HIM** After you've climaxed, let me rip your panties off and jump on top to give you orgasm number two.

# ...*show off your muscles*

Kinky Dares

# 317

**HER** Thrill me with your strong muscles and your manly ability to throw me into any position you like.

**HIM** Let's work our way through the standing positions, then the sitting ones....

*...get high on oral*

**318**

**HER** Marvel at my bar work and reward me by burying your face between my legs and kissing me passionately.

**HIM** Get to a point of feverish arousal, then come down for some delirious sex.

# ...*sit in the naughty chair*

# 319

**HER** Delight me with your tongue and fingers through the straps of a sex chair.

**HIM** Reach forward and give me hand-over-hand strokes on my penis.

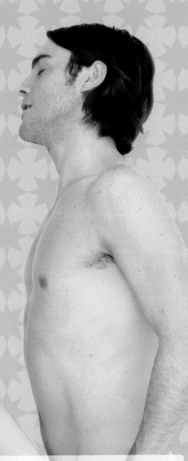

# ...give some firm back-up

## 320

**HER** Turn me on by pressing your erection naughtily between my cheeks.

**HIM** Massage me with lots of lube first so we can experiment with anal entry.

*...make bunny love*

# 321

**HER** Make me your bad bunny girl. Pull me onto your lap, slide your hands up my thighs, and tell me how much you want me.

**HIM** Be naughty and sexy, but play hard to get. Make me work to seduce you.

# ...go in the hard way

## 322

**HER** Do a forward bend, then gently bend your penis back and slip the tip inside me.

**HIM** Drive me to distraction by grinding your hips hard against me.

# ...be a very bad cop

## 323

**HER** Prepare for a strip search as I point my pistol at your package.

**HIM** Be mean: order me to lie on the floor then place your heel on my chest and your handcuffs on my wrists.

*...give him some head space*

**324**

**HER** Give me some intense "behind-the-scenes" oral sex.

**HIM** Gaze ahead of you and abandon yourself to an extremely naughty fantasy.

*...enjoy her hang ups*

**325**

**HER** Support me in your arms as I get a rush from hanging upside down. Press your lips to my clitoris and kiss me hard.

**HIM** Align your head with my penis and kiss me feverishly.

# ...start slave training

## 326

**HER** Train me in the art of submission. Penetrate me as I lie across your lap and threaten me with your whip if I disobey you.

**HIM** Get completely into character: address me only as "master".

# ...take your tongue
# for a walk

## 327

**HER** Position me over a sex ramp and then move your tongue in a slow meandering line from my vagina to my anus.

**HIM** Do the same to me, but start by flicking your tongue lightly across my balls.

# ...try a squeaky clean seduction

## 328

**HER** Get a kick out of watching me scrub the floor on my hands and knees.

**HIM** Work up a sweat wearing your sexiest lingerie, then sit back and provocatively unclasp your bra.

*...be a naughty devil*

**329**

**HER** Use your devilish charm to lure, coax, and tempt me into wickedness.

**HIM** Start by bending over so I can give you a hot spank with my trident.

## ...have each other in the hall

**330**

**HER** Pounce on me as soon as I walk through the door – rip my clothes off and have raunchy sex with me in the hall.

**HIM** Lean forward and brace yourself against the wall as I make a smooth entry.

*...make
her stay
at home*

# 331

**HER** Give me a surprise seduction just as I'm all dressed up and ready to go out.

**HIM** Let me pin you to the spot by caressing you with a vibrator on max setting,

# ...stand and deliver

## 332

**HER** Make me moan with pleasure as you pick me up from the bed and slide me on to your erection.

**HIM** Throw your head back and get carried away with the intensity of the mood.

# ...try reverse cowgirl

Kinky Dares

**333**

**HER** Lie on your back while I saddle up with my back to you. Squeeze my bum as I ride.

**HIM** Make the ride even more raunchy by talking dirty to me.

# ...try a bit of rough

## 334

**HER** Let me ravish you with my teeth and nails. Moan with delight as I scratch, bite, and rake your skin.

**HIM** Lay me on my back and lightly graze my penis with your teeth.

*...try the rainbow position*

**335**

**HER** Send pleasure arcing through my body – enter incredibly slowly as I bend over backwards for you.

**HIM** Arch your back and lift your pelvis high so I can admire your exquisite curves.

...try
"banging in
a nail"

**336**

**HER** Let's try a Kama Sutra classic: you enter me in a kneeling position while I rest my heel on your forehead.

**HIM** Open yourself up to me as I bang in the nail with fervour.

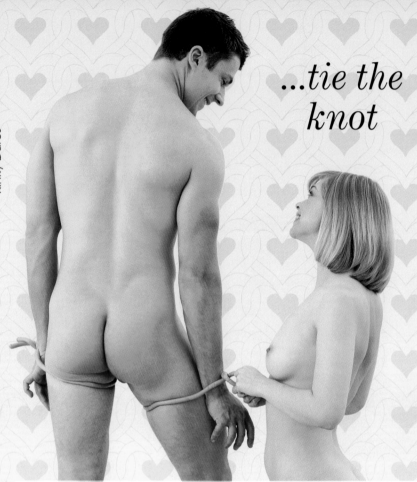

*...tie the knot*

# 337

**HER** Sneak up behind me and secure my hands behind my back with spank ties. Now do what you like with me.

**HIM** When it's my turn, wind the spank ties around my wrists and thighs.

*...take the seat of power*

# 338

**HER** Roll back into a half-shoulderstand and then gently bend your erection back through your thighs for me to sit on.

**HIM** Exploit your position: bounce hard on me and slap my thigh.

# ...do the "grasshopper"

## 339

**HER** Stimulate erogenous spots I didn't know I had – enter me back-to-front as I tuck my knees in to my chest.

**HIM** Make me jerk with pleasure by rippling your internal muscles along my shaft.

# ...*march him to boot camp*

## 340

**HER** Put your arms behind your back and let me frog march you to the bedroom.

**HIM** Bark orders at me. Make me do naked push-ups, and punish me if I fail.

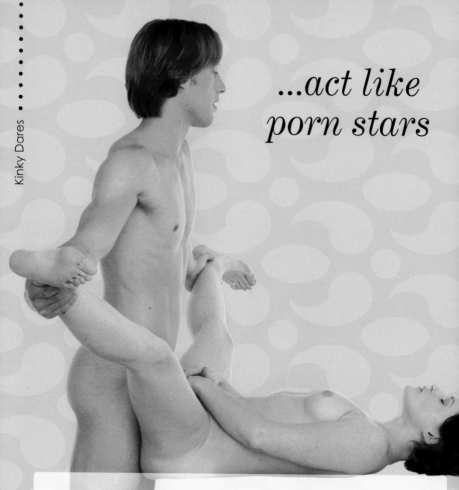

...*act like porn stars*

**341**

**HER** Grab my legs and pull them wide apart as you thrust dramatically inside me.

**HIM** Pretend you're performing for a camera – pant, moan, and writhe.

# ...set off a chain reaction

**342**

**HER** Give me a sharp shot of ecstasy by clamping my nipples and then pulling the chain – take me to my pain limit.

**HIM** At the peak of arousal wiggle your bum back so I can slide deep inside you.

*...have a bit on the side*

## 343

**HER** Give me sexy shudders by picking me up and penetrating me from the side.

**HIM** Let me lower you to the floor to discover other thrilling side angles.

# ...give a French polish

**344**

**HER** Throw yourself into a kinky roleplay – you're the naked businessman and I'm your hot French maid.

**HIM** Tickle my chest with your feather duster – go lower as I get aroused.

# ...experiment with beads

## 345

**HER** Let me make you convulse with pleasure by pushing anal beads inside you one by one.

**HIM** Take me to the brink of orgasm and then slowly pull the beads out.

# ...target her A-spot

**346**

**HER** Take me to heaven with fingertip explorations of my A-spot – search for the highest point on the front wall of my vagina.

**HIM** When I've discovered it with my fingers let me target it with my penis.

# ...*reverse roles for the night*

## 347

**HER** Get down on all fours so I can enjoy the thrilling naughtiness of being the penetrator.

**HIM** Massage my bum with lots of lube to give a smooth entry that makes me buckle with pleasure.

*...find the perfect alignment*

**348**

**HER** Let me sit on the stairs while you find the step that makes you the perfect height to penetrate me.

**HIM** When I've found it, rest your foot on my shoulder so I can go in deep.

# ...play the mean mistress

## 349

**HER** Lie still with your wrists and ankles bound while I tempt you with my body.

**HIM** Entice me by getting close then pulling away. Run your hands seductively over your hips and breasts.

*...invent a new type of 69*

**350**

**HER** Let's take a creative approach to 69 – sit back on a chair so I can position myself on top of you.

**HIM** Give me the ultimate turn on: squeeze your thighs around my face as you lick me.

## ...try kinky yoga

**351**

**HER** Let me get into a hot yoga position like the bridge pose. Take me to new heights of pleasure with your fingers and thumbs.

**HIM** Let me give you an orgasm that brings you crashing to the floor.

# ...make it anonymous

## 352

**HER** Keep your eyes closed as I back on to your erection and then use you for my pleasure.

**HIM** Relish the naughty thrill of sex that's faceless – pretend you don't know me.

# ...have foot fetish sex

## 353

**HER** Make me writhe with glorious sensations – penetrate me, then lean forward, and kiss and bite my toes.

**HIM** Let's discover a sex position that lets you lick my toes, too.

# ...do it with restraints

## 354

**HER** Bind my wrists with a spank tie, then throw me on some cushions and move inside me with fast, darting strokes.

**HIM** Restrain my wrists for round two, then sit on top as I lie back in bliss.

*...surrender all control*

# 355

**HER** Make me tremble with erotic vulnerabilty by blindfolding me and pushing me to the floor.

**HIM** Don't try to predict what I'm going to do – just enjoy the thrill of being dominated.

*...experiment with the furniture*

**356**

**HER** Put a foot stool in the middle of the bedroom – invite me in for some sexy fun.

**HIM** Let me give you sensational spasms as you kneel on top of the stool and lean forward with your hands on the floor.

*...hang out and talk dirty*

**357**

**HER** Let me grab you with my legs as I hang from a bar. Now pull me close and whisper some filthy suggestions.

**HIM** Tell me in x-rated terms how turned on you are. Then let me penetrate you hard.

...*try advanced level oral*

# 358

**HER** Let me dazzle you with my sexpertise. Give me glorious licks as you lower your head between my legs.

**HIM** Hook your legs over my shoulders and stay there as long as you can.

*...use a paddle*

# 359

**HER** Let's take spanking to the next level. Make my cheeks blush with a professional spanking paddle.

**HIM** Swap places so I can feel the sweet stinging sensation, too.

# ...play her B-side

**360**

**HER** Lavish lube upon your penis then slowly enter me anally as I lie in "rabbit" position.

**HIM** Let your body relax completely so you can take me in deep.

# ...experiment with rubber

## 361

**HER** Close your eyes while I sink to my knees and manhandle you with rubber gloves on.

**HIM** Make your touch warm and slippery – dip your gloved hands in hot water first.

*...dress
for the
occasion*

# 362

**HER** Throw a fetish party for two in our bedroom. Buy me something kinky to wear.

**HIM** Get an erotic kick as I fasten a studded leather dog collar around your neck. Prepare to be dominated.

*...play dog and mistress*

**363**

**HER** Get down on your hands and knees behind me and surprise me with your unrestrained passion.

**HIM** Stand still while I devour you with hungry bites.

## ...make it military

**364**

**HER** Let me make your pulse race by parading for you in military-style undies.

**HIM** Let me give you a very intimate inspection followed by a strict drill in the bedroom.

# ...get an erotic close-up

## 365

**HER** Let me squat on top of you so I can see all the hot action as I bob up and down.

**HIM** Let's have back-to-front sex so I can lean forward and be thrilled by the sexiest view imaginable.

# Go shopping online

Preparing for an evening of sex dares is all part of the fun. So whether you're shopping for whipped cream and honey, or handcuffs and bondage tape, enjoy the sexy build-up to a night of pleasure. Best of all: take your partner online shopping, and make your shopping list as naughty and indulgent as you dare.

Start with these:

www.myla.com
www.coco-de-mer.com
www.agentprovocateur.com
www.jimmyjane.com
www.pullupbar.org.uk
www.lovehoney.co.uk
www.annsummers.com
www.emotionalbliss.co.uk
www.lelo.com

And if you fancy some erotic reading material while you're shopping:

www.erotica-uk.com
www.emandlo.com
www.scarletmagazine.co.uk

# Dare selector

| | | | | | | | | |
|---|---|---|---|---|---|---|---|---|
| 231 | 188 | 32 | 350 | 260 | 308 | 145 | 74 | 248 |
| 349 | 70 | 253 | 242 | 121 | 316 | 4 | 84 | 301 | 361 |
| 357 | 130 | 177 | 21 | 122 | 218 | 14 | 348 | 167 |
| 165 | 311 | 62 | 78 | 136 | 186 | 81 | 352 | 119 |
| 86 | 336 | 317 | 143 | 85 | 297 | 22 | 323 | 220 |
| 79 | 332 | 270 | 189 | 19 | 155 | 222 | 54 | 196 |
| 236 | 99 | 325 | 267 | 38 | 292 | 42 | 329 | 113 |
| 315 | 61 | 327 | 226 | 341 | 354 | 106 | 27 | 345 |
| 320 | 271 | 313 | 97 | 91 | 230 | 139 | 201 | 137 |
| 3 | 279 | 193 | 351 | 83 | 333 | 100 | 264 | 294 |
| 59 | 93 | 310 | 258 | 306 | 303 | 195 | 101 | 197 |
| 46 | 10 | 24 | 17 | 307 | 173 | 262 | 364 | 82 | 142 |
| 154 | 198 | 247 | 347 | 41 | 127 | 63 | 276 | 275 |
| 250 | 6 | 252 | 131 | 245 | 180 | 172 | 229 | 64 |
| 75 | 109 | 40 | 344 | 65 | 183 | 223 | 228 | 255 |
| 133 | 282 | 240 | 67 | 144 | 298 | 176 | 135 | 110 |
| 34 | 25 | 338 | 318 | 138 | 153 | 90 | 274 | 114 |
| 13 | 28 | 346 | 166 | 211 | 232 | 148 | 36 | 335 |
| 147 | 326 | 305 | 337 | 182 | 234 | 266 | 44 | 233 |
| 57 | 115 | 47 | 289 | 204 | 246 | 355 | 272 | 141 |

*To pick tonight's dare, close your eyes and see where your finger lands.*

| 199 | 268 | 273 | 302 | 221 | 150 | 331 | 10 |
| 290 | 365 | 58 | 285 | 190 | 261 | 11 | 162 | 18 |
| 237 | 278 | 210 | 225 | 288 | 68 | 339 | 49 | 13 |
| 118 | 251 | 124 | 128 | 157 | 156 | 194 | 2 | 7 |
| 213 | 187 | 66 | 235 | 269 | 163 | 179 | 140 | 25 |
| 112 | 20 | 111 | 319 | 322 | 52 | 159 | 73 | 25 |
| 39 | 31 | 152 | 321 | 103 | 37 | 263 | 219 | 14 |
| 178 | 48 | 287 | 238 | 191 | 300 | 291 | 96 | 16 |
| 116 | 296 | 174 | 205 | 88 | 309 | 284 | 160 | 20 |
| 181 | 340 | 209 | 26 | 227 | 23 | 239 | 123 | 27 |
| 158 | 45 | 107 | 283 | 168 | 125 | 72 | 330 | 36 |
| 185 | 241 | 353 | 51 | 43 | 105 | 7 | 69 | 342 | 3 |
| 356 | 108 | 200 | 129 | 8 | 30 | 18 | 359 | 360 | 5 |
| 314 | 212 | 286 | 89 | 5 | 170 | 120 | 265 | 98 | 33 |
| 358 | 87 | 146 | 77 | 132 | 175 | 295 | 102 | 30 |
| 16 | 281 | 324 | 217 | 12 | 216 | 208 | 56 | 17 |
| 95 | 244 | 126 | 254 | 92 | 206 | 80 | 169 | 24 |
| 224 | 299 | 117 | 29 | 9 | 1 | 94 | 215 | 164 | 24 |
| 362 | 35 | 343 | 202 | 256 | 312 | 280 | 71 | 20 |
| 151 | 293 | 214 | 60 | 15 | 328 | 55 | 192 | 5 |

It is assumed that couples are monogamous and have been tested for sexually transmitted infections. Always practise safe and responsible sex, and consult a doctor if you have a condition that might preclude strenuous sexual activity. Challenging intercourse positions might put a strain on your back or other body parts – do not attempt them if you have injuries or ailments and consult your doctor for advice beforehand if you are concerned. Sex in public places should only be undertaken with due consideration of the law and the sensibilities of others. The author and publisher do not accept any responsibility for any injury or ailment caused by following any of the suggestions contained in this book.

DK would like to thank Charlotte Seymour for initial design styling and Kate Meeker for editorial assistance.

Special thanks to Kesta Desmond.